MEDICAL PRACTICE MANAGEMENT
Body of Knowledge Review

HUMAN RESOURCE MANAGEMENT

VOLUME 3

MGMA
104 Inverness Terrace East
Englewood, CO 80112-5306
877.275.6462
mgma.org

Medical Group Management Association® (MGMA®) publications are intended to provide current and accurate information and are designed to assist readers in becoming more familiar with the subject matter covered. Such publications are distributed with the understanding that MGMA does not render any legal, accounting, or other professional advice that may be construed as specifically applicable to individual situations. No representations nor warranties are made concerning the application of legal or other principles discussed by the authors to any specific factual situation, nor is any prediction made concerning how any particular judge, government official, or other person who will interpret or apply such principles. Specific factual situations should be discussed with professional advisors.

Library of Congress Cataloging-in-Publication Data
Human resource management (2015)
Human resource management.
p. ; cm. -- (Medical practice management body of knowledge review (Third edition) ; volume 3)
Includes bibliographical references and index.
ISBN 978-1-56829-448-3
I. MGMA (Association), issuing body. II. Title. III. Series: Medical practice management body of knowledge review (Third edition) ; v. 3.
[DNLM: 1. Practice Management, Medical--organization & administration. 2. Health Manpower--organization & administration. 3. Personnel Management--methods. W 80]
R728
610.68--dc23
2015020356

Item: 8822
ISBN: 978-1-56829-448-3

Printed in the United States of America

10 9 8 7 6 5 4 3 2 1

Body of Knowledge Review Series — Third Edition

VOLUME 1 Operations Management

VOLUME 2 Financial Management

VOLUME 3 Human Resource Management

VOLUME 4 Organizational Governance and Patient-Centered Care

VOLUME 5 Risk and Compliance Management

Contents

Introduction

Managing people, from hiring through training and performance management, must be a core competency for every medical practice administrator. And while many of the same regulations and skills are required for managers in any organization, there are particular nuances specific to the delivery of healthcare in a clinic setting that differentiate the medical practice administrator from his or her peers in other business or healthcare delivery environments. The chapters in this volume follow the blueprint designed by practicing medical practice executives to describe the key competencies, knowledge, and skills needed to develop and maintain effective operations in the medical practice.

The certified and fellow members of the Medical Group Management Association (MGMA®) identified the major areas of competence in human resource management as:

- Creating, implementing, and managing a staffing plan;
- Directing and managing the retention of clinical and nonclinical staff;
- Training and developing clinical and nonclinical staff and understanding employment law;
- Developing and implementing staff compensation and benefit plans; and
- Managing and evaluating the performance of staff.

Within each chapter of this volume, these major competencies are further delineated according to the key knowledge and skills required to *demonstrate* competency as a manager of human resources. A few examples of these supporting skills are the ability to identify, analyze, and maintain the appropriate number of clinical and nonclinical staff members with the correct mix of skills; manage employee motivation and teamwork to obtain high performance; and comply with employment laws. This knowledge, these skills, and much more are explored in detail in the pages that follow.

Chapter 1

The Staffing Plan

Staffing a medical office requires a strong understanding of staff skills and abilities as they relate to organizational goals. The number of staff members as well as their skill sets should also be tied to organizational goals. The types of staff members needed relates to the skill mix and knowledge that the practice requires. Key skills required to effectively manage a medical practice staffing plan include the ability to establish job classification systems, identify the appropriate number and types of staff members, use benchmarking data, oversee the recruitment and orientation process, evaluate candidates, and establish an effective selection process.

Keeping Up with Changes in the Organization and Labor Market

Jobs evolve over time and new types of jobs may emerge. A medical practice needs to change with the times and be open to employment changes based on the needs of the practice. Twenty years ago, no one in a medical practice would have considered hiring either a chief information officer or a telephone triage nurse. However, with the growth of information technology and automated applications, people in both positions are often needed.

Expectations also change over time. A medical secretary hired to transcribe medical notes and answer the telephone for a physician may need to change job functions when talk technology eliminates the need for transcription and a call center is developed to answer the telephone. An employee who doesn't adapt well to change will become a liability instead of an asset when change is required within the practice.

Shortages in the labor pool create tremendous strain on the medical practice and may limit the practice's ability to meet current or growing patient needs. With a shortage of radiology technologists, a medical practice may not be able to expand hours of operation in the evenings or on weekends. Medical practice managers need to keep tabs on the needs of the practice and the labor market to help guide hiring decisions and prepare for internal and external change.

Planning for Staffing Needs

Creating a staffing plan is not an isolated activity. Practices must incorporate it into all the plans the business makes.

Strategic and Business Plans

A strategic plan followed by a detailed business plan will help a medical practice address its changing needs over time. A strategic plan is usually created for a three- to five-year period and articulates the practice's vision for the future. For example, the medical practice may have an aging medical group and need to recruit younger physicians. The vision of physician recruitment should be integrated into a business plan for the recruitment process. Planning for the future helps the medical group become proactive and not reactive to a changing environment.

If a medical practice is open eight hours a day and five days a week, the space is used only 24 percent of the time. If a medical practice wants to expand its productivity, it can either see more patients every hour or expand its hours of operation. Developing a second medical office location for the practice can be an expensive endeavor unless the practice decides to pilot a new location through a time-share arrangement in which a physician shares space with another physician who already has an established practice.

The human resource department may lead a strategic effort toward disseminated authority or may require decisions to be made by a board of directors or a senior physician or administrative leader. Because the human resource department is a cost center, careful consideration is made on what the cost and benefits are for a particular decision.

Budget Plans

Eighty percent of a medical practice's budget may be focused on staffing. This creates huge challenges for the medical administrator to provide qualified, well-trained staff members at a competitive price. A medical practice executive should consider how overtime, shift differential pay, and employee status (part time vs. full time) affect the bottom line in short- and long-term budgets.

Scheduling Plans

Staffing is both an art and a science. Developing an effective schedule based on staffing mix, hours needed, and skills performed will work if there are enough staff members to draw from. A mix of full-time, part-time, and as-needed staff members who can work days, evenings, and weekends provide scheduling flexibility for the practice manager.

Schedules can vary based on physician or patient needs. Medical practices may vary employee shifts and hours based on employee preferences. For example, an employee may be attracted to three 12-hour shifts because it allows that employee to be off four days during the week, even though the employee has to work long hours for three days. In contrast, another employee may want only eight-hour shifts because of limitations in day care. Even though flexible schedules are logistically challenging, they can be strong employee satisfiers. Rotating shifts so that employees work every third weekend may be preferable to required weekend shifts every week. These flexible schedule blocks can meet employee needs and meet the needs of the organization to provide staffing during nontraditional hours.

Determining the Types of Jobs Needed to Run the Practice

The creation of job description and classifications for the practice is a multifaceted process. First, based on the strategic planning of the practice, the types of jobs currently needed and those needed in the future are identified. Next, each job is analyzed according to its vital components — the what, why, and how of the job. Finally, each job's responsibilities, qualifications, and relationships are described. This allows you to classify the jobs into categories and to move on the next steps of evaluating job worth to determine compensation rates.

When analyzing jobs, focus on the key job elements including duties, supervision received and exercised, interpersonal relationship involved, level of difficulty, impact of errors, physical demands, working conditions, and qualifications. After considering all these factors, your task is to succinctly state the essential functions of the job. This information is critical in all human resource management functions: recruiting, training, supervision, and performance management.

Job Classification

Categorizing the various jobs into classes helps to improve efficiency and productivity. This process is called *job classification.*

Job classification is a tool that groups similar jobs together to make them easier to manage. For example, a bookstore is categorized according to genre (i.e., travel, cooking, fiction, self-help, and so on) so shoppers can easily identify which types of books are where. Job classifications define which job descriptions fit into a specific category. For example, an administrative class of jobs might include all the positions whose duties are to perform, under supervision, difficult and responsible administrative work in an office, business, or finance setting.

More specifically, job classification is the process of grouping job positions that have duties and responsibilities of a similar nature into classes. It involves slotting job descriptions into a series of classes that cover the range of jobs in your organization. Each class should be detailed enough to be descriptive, yet still general enough not to be limiting.

Job classification helps you make human resource decisions related to recruiting, selection, promotion, equal employment opportunities, performance evaluation, training and developing, and compensation. Job classification helps specifically with compensation decisions when, for example, you must:

- Determine the relative worth of the various jobs in the practice;
- Establish a pay plan that incorporates appropriate differentials among jobs; or
- Guard against pay inequities.

Job Analysis

Job analysis is the systematic process of collecting and making certain judgments about all of the important information related to a specific job. The designated human resource professional should execute a job analysis when the practice needs to create a new position, upgrade a traditional position, or completely transform a position into something different.

Job analysis helps everyone gain a better understanding of the content of an individual's work, the relationship of the work to the practice, and the qualifications the individual must have to fulfill all of the job tasks. Analyzing all of the jobs in the practice assists you in managing human resource responsibilities and helps managers and employees understand more fully the nature of the practice's work.

The analysis involves identifying exactly which skills an employee must have in order to fulfill the requirements of the job. When analyzing jobs, the following parameters should be defined:

- Essential functions and related duties;
- Profession or occupation involved;
- Nonsupervisory responsibilities;
- Supervisory and administrative responsibilities;
- Physical demands;
- Accountabilities and desired outcomes;
- Working conditions;
- Technology requirements;
- Necessary knowledge (learned through education and experience), skills (demonstration of knowledge), and abilities (capacity for learning and doing);
- Appropriate behaviors; and
- Performance standards.

The Americans with Disabilities Act (ADA) of 1990 brought to light the importance of a worker's qualification to do a job. Unless you can identify the essential functions of a position, you could inadvertently discriminate against someone who can do the job despite a disability.

Job Analysis Steps

A job analysis requires the following three steps:

1. **Job identification.** Indicate the job title, job status, job code (if any), pay range, geographic location, and immediate supervisory reporting structure. In analyzing the skills needed, consider factors such as education, independent judgment, and initiative.
2. **Job description.** Describe the job tasks, reporting structure, physical requirements (including dexterity and motor skills, standing, twisting, sitting, reaching, bending, and lifting), and working conditions (i.e., the general work environment where the job will be performed, including job hazards). When describing the job duties and responsibilities, consider who assigns and supervises the work, as well as what the worker does. It is also important to know the level of difficulty of the job, the impact of error, and the interpersonal working relationships involved.
3. **Job qualifications.** Indicate the qualifications needed for successful job performance. It should be clear that workers have the knowledge, skills, and abilities that match the essential job functions; they should be able to perform the job successfully. Essential functions are typically listed on the performance evaluation form so that there is a direct link between what is expected of jobholders and how they perform the job.

   Generally, the designated human resource professional coordinates the job analysis process with employees and their supervisors helping to collect detailed information about each position. A consultant who is a specialist in job analysis could also be hired. Methods for conducting a job analysis include questionnaires, interviews, checklists, diaries, observations, activity samplings, and critical incidents.

   Sometimes an organization uses personal interviews to collect information when conducting job analyses. Interviewing each employee can be time consuming and expensive if using a consultant but can provide more complete and accurate information. To obtain high-quality information, the interviewer must be highly skilled and experienced in conducting job analysis interviews.

Job Descriptions

Many terms are used for job descriptions: *position descriptions* (a job description personalized for one specific individual), *job specifications* (all of the details of a job including knowledge, skills, and abilities needed), and *job descriptions* (a list of the job tasks, duties, and responsibilities). Typically, a job description encompasses all of these other terms and is the term used here.

Complete, current, and detailed job descriptions help new workers understand their jobs and remind existing employees what is expected of them. They guide employee selection and placement, help assess training and development needs, and serve as the foundation for performance standards. Formal job descriptions also protect organizations from charges of discrimination because they clearly detail what workers must be able to do as required by the ADA.

The Medical Group Management Association (MGMA®) Career Center is a great and thorough resource for learning about, developing, and updating job descriptions. To ensure that your medical practice follows through with job classifications, including job analyses and job descriptions, it is useful to have a job classification policy.

Hiring the Correct Number and Types of Staff Members

MGMA's annual *Performance and Practices of Successful Medical Groups* show that understaffing or overstaffing medical group both are directly correlated to lower financial performance.[1]

Low staffing levels constrain physician productivity. Physicians in understaffed practices may be more involved in nonclinical, administrative tasks and may lack the necessary infrastructure to support their clinical productivity and efficiency, reducing profitability. In addition, low staffing levels can present a business risk to a medical group if they introduce greater variability in work processes and performance, lead to problematic patient access and service, and create poor staff morale that results in high staff turnover.

At the highest levels of staffing, the data show that the increased cost of staff does not translate to higher performance as measured by revenue after operating cost.[2] Better performing medical groups are those that have identified the best number and best mix of staff to support physician productivity and create a positive financial effect on the medical group.

It is generally agreed that employees in the medical practice are the practice's most valuable resource. It matters how the telephone scheduler interacts with the patient to promote ease of access to the practice. It matters if patients are greeted and warmly welcomed to the practice, or if they are treated like numbers or diseases. It matters that the nurse reflects empathy and concern and assists the physician in caring for the patient as a human being, not just as a customer.

Some researchers have identified a "mirror" phenomenon associated with employee satisfaction and customer satisfaction.[3] That is, when high levels of employee satisfaction are reported, high levels of customer satisfaction are also found. This mirror test holds true in the medical practice. Rightsizing creates a tremendous effect on employee satisfaction. Employees who feel frenzied or too hurried in their job assignments rarely report high job satisfaction. However, it is equally important to recognize that rightsizing staff has implications for patient satisfaction, a critical performance measure of medical practices today.

Problems of Too Few Staff Members

The consequences of having two few staff members are numerous. Staff recruitment and retention are difficult for practices with too few staff members. Employees are highly mobile, and they can seek alternative employment with practices that have appropriate staffing and workload levels.

Physician productivity will also decline with too few staff members, because physicians will spend significant time on nonclinical, administrative tasks instead of providing healthcare services. Most practices can ill afford for their physicians to not be actively engaged in the clinical practice of medicine.

Too few staff members also can lead to problematic patient service. Asking staff members to handle more than an appropriate work level or scope of work will negatively affect patient service (and possibly patient safety). Staff members cannot be customer minded when they are racing through the day attempting to meet unrealistic workload demands.

A practice may also increase its business risk when it has an insufficient number of staff members or an inappropriate skill mix of staff members. Examples of the risk a practice faces when it has too few staff members include declines in the quality of patient care services, failure to appropriately manage the acuity level of patients, and overlooking important details. Also, when employees are asked to perform their tasks too quickly, internal controls may be deemphasized and there is a tendency to cut corners. Medical practices with too few staff members often resort to high levels of multitasking that typically result in low levels of accountability, because no one person can be held accountable for performance results. Thus, too few staff members may lead to preventable business risk. It may also lead to expensive human resource issues, such as excessive sick leave, labor issues, or lawsuits because staff members are required to perform workload levels or skill levels well beyond their current capability or training.

Problems of Too Many Staff Members

The consequences of having too many staff members are also significant. A key question that should be asked is: *Do the staff members act to influence physician productivity, or are they occupied with tasks that do not add value for the patient?* Staffing is a measure of work, thus the staffing levels would be expected to vary based on medical and surgical procedures performed in the practice, work relative value units, and other measures of physician work levels.

When there is an overabundance of staff members, employees become accustomed to low workload levels. This makes it difficult to step up to higher levels of productivity. Many practices have too many staff members because their staffing plan is based on meeting the maximum expected patient load at all times when, in fact, patient volume fluctuates.

There is obviously a financial impact associated with too many staff members as well. Support staff expenditures as a percentage of total medical revenue are high for those practices with too many staff members. Staffing cost is one of the highest expenditures in the medical practice, typically ranging from 12 percent of total medical revenue for cardiovascular surgery to 32 percent for family practice,[4] so actively managing staffing cost levels is important for practice profitability.

The practice's inability to adjust staff levels with the workload in the practice also represents a high-cost staffing model. Some practices do not fluctuate their staffing consistent with physician schedules and the actual workload. For example, if surgeons are in the operating room on Tuesdays and Thursdays, then why does the practice need all of its staff members in the office setting on those days? If Friday afternoons are lightly scheduled, why isn't staffing flexed to correspond with the lightened workload? Practices may argue that employees need this time to catch up. However, medical practices today do not typically have the financial luxury of providing catch-up time for staff when the physician is not scheduled.

A final example of failure to match staffing with physician workload are those practices where physicians may work a four- or four-and-one-half-day workweek in the office, and the clinical support staff employees are flexed off with their physician, yet the staff members still report full-time hours because of overtime incurred during the workweek. This scenario does not permit the medical practice to take advantage of fluctuating work schedules and financial savings consistent with physician work levels.

Linking Staff to Physician Work Levels

The key to efficient staffing models and staffing deployment is to recognize that staffing is a measure of work. That is, the volume of staff and the skill mix of staff vary based on physician and practice work levels. Historically, many practices have attempted to provide the same number of nurses or the same number of medical assistants to each physician working in the practice. Physicians have different levels of productivity and perform different scopes of service that, in turn, may require different levels of staff support. The historical staffing models have been supplanted by newer approaches that assign staff based on physician work levels, with many medical practices adopting staffing models involving shared or centralized staff support functions.

Accounting for Varying Staff Skill Levels

A match of the employee's skills to the actual work that needs to be performed in the medical practice is also required for appropriate right-sizing of the practice. Using a registered nurse simply to room patients and function as a medical assistant is not a good use of resources for the practice. Similarly, if a medical assistant is asked to perform nursing duties, that model would present a business risk and potentially affect quality of care. The goal is to match the skills required for the particular job function or task and to delegate appropriate levels of responsibility to support staff members within the scope of their classification and licensure.

Internal Factors That Determine Proper Staffing Levels

Staffing levels are also determined by a host of internal, medical practice–specific factors that are qualitative in nature. The following four key areas at the microsystem level of the medical practice affect staff rightsizing.

1. The Practice Model

The practice model is the method by which the physicians have elected (or have been directed) to practice medicine. This encompasses a number of areas including:

- Whether the medical practice is organized as a true group practice (or simply individual practices that have been colocated);
- The number of practice sites in which physicians work;
- The skill mix of staff that has been requested or provided to the physician;
- The types of duties that have been delegated to staff; and
- The extent to which specific tasks are shared or distributed.

The practice model that has been adopted will have a direct effect on staffing strategies employed in the medical practice. For example, for practices that have designated a one-to-one assignment of a nurse to a physician (with the nurse performing telephone nurse triage, managing the prescription refill process, managing test results reporting, and performing other functions), the practice has limited alternatives when the nurse must be absent from work. Typically these practices secure registry staff or *float pool* staff to provide nursing coverage for the physician. A change to the practice model involving shared nurse triage or establishment of a nurse advice unit and the creation of systematic processes to manage prescription refills or test results reporting, for example, may permit a wider range of options for clinical support and may also serve to enhance patient service.

2. Patient Scheduling

Differences in staffing support volumes and skill mix are also caused by the type of patient scheduling model that is employed. For example, if a physician has adopted a sophisticated scheduling system, such as modified wave scheduling or advanced access scheduling, then the scheduling staff is highly engaged in bringing patients into the practice and optimizing the efficiency of the physician.

An example of the effect of patient scheduling on staffing is provided in Exhibit 1.1. The data reflect the number of patients scheduled and the total number of hours from when the first patient is scheduled to when the last patient is scheduled during the day for five family practice physicians who have similar practices, including similar new-to-return patient ratios, similar volume of physicals, and so forth. During this particular week, there was high variability in average patients per scheduled hour of time. While some of this variability may be caused by physician variation in practice style, the data suggest that there may be opportunities to enhance patient scheduling to improve physician efficiency. Large blocks of time during the day that are not scheduled efficiently will affect the ability of the physician to optimize efficiency, productivity, and revenue.

In Exhibit 1.1, the clinical staff support provided to each of the physicians in the practice includes both a registered nurse and a medical assistant. There would appear to be a significant amount of idle time during the day for some of these staff members when patients are not seen. In this example, staffing utilization could be optimized with reductions in variability in how patients are scheduled throughout the day. If the patient scheduling process does not change, then adopting a group practice focus toward clinical staffing should be explored, consistent with the variability in patient volume per scheduled hour.

3. The Practice's Facility

Space may be a limiting factor in a medical practice's ability to optimize staffing levels. An examination of the role facility design plays in enhancing productivity of the organization reveals variation among better performing medical practices and other practices. Better performing medical groups understand the importance of facility design in minimizing travel time by physicians in the practice and in optimizing exam room space to minimize wasted or unproductive time for the physician.

EXHIBIT 1.1

Average Patients per Scheduled Hour per Physician[5]

Physician	Monday	Tuesday	Wednesday	Thursday	Friday	Average Patients/ Scheduled Hour
Dr. A						
Patients	19	16	21	Not in	25	**5.14**
Scheduled Hours	4.5	3.0	5.25	clinic	3.0	
Dr. B						
Patients	24	24	23	Not in	21	**3.09**
Scheduled Hours	7.25	8.25	8.25	clinic	6.0	
Dr. C						
Patients	18	13	21	Not in	27	**3.40**
Scheduled Hours	7.0	2.75	7.0	clinic	6.5	
Dr. D						
Patients	23	Not in	26	21	19	**3.04**
Scheduled Hours	7.5	clinic	7.75	7.0	7.0	
Dr. E						
Patients	30	34	24	31	26	**3.74**
Scheduled Hours	7.0	8.25	7.25	8.0	8.25	

4. The Practice's Ability to Leverage Technology

Information technology and/or the ability to leverage technology may limit the capability of a practice to achieve efficient staffing levels. If the medical practice has an electronic medical record, it will also affect the flow of staff in the practice. For example, with electronic medical records, the medical records personnel are not involved in chart retrieval and courier functions but instead spend time ensuring closed-loop processes for document scanning, patient notes, and so forth.

Using Benchmarks to Determine Proper Staffing Levels

The number of staff members needed can be tied to benchmarking data of like organizations. A new physician will not require two new staff members, and a pediatrician practicing at the 90th percentile of production may need more than two staff members to support the practice. The number of staff members should be based on productivity measures, hours of operation, skills required, available technology, and other resources within the group. For example, a practice that has an electronic health record and automated telephone response system in place may not need the same number of staff members as a practice of the same size that has paper medical records and no telephone automation.

Full-time equivalent (FTE) ratios provide a benchmark for the medical practice to follow. They may be guidelines or measures of productivity, production, and/or efficiency. For example, 4.5 FTEs per physician may be a good ratio for a physician achieving production at the 99th percentile, but a bad ratio for a physician at the 10th percentile. FTE ratios can help the medical practice guide staffing decisions and outcomes.

MGMA provides resources, such as the book *Innovative Staffing for the Medical Practice* and the MGMA DataDive: Cost and Revenue Modules, that benchmark physician-to-staff ratios based on numerous factors, such as physician specialty, medical ownership, and practice size.[6] A busy family practice physician seeing 40 patients a day will require more staff members than a busy urologist seeing 15 patients a day because of the volume of patients seen in a primary care vs. specialty care practice.[7] In addition, the staff ratio needs to be broken down with respect to the types of people needed to ensure that the appropriate mix of staff skills is available to support the physician.

Planning workforce needs is both an art and a science. Staff ratios may meet benchmarked data, but they may still be ineffective if the staff members are not well trained and other resources of automation, coordination, and teamwork are not in place.

Staffing Strategies

Knowing when it is the right time to bring on new staff is always a challenge. Sometimes staff members complain that they are overworked and need additional staff. That overworked perception may be specific to a particular day, because of understaffed departments as a result of vacations or from additional tasks that have been assumed because of a special project with a strict deadline. It is critical for the medical practice executive to assess the needs of a department and determine under what circumstances and timing the staff may need more help.

Some organizations have a structure and culture that does not allow certain staffing changes to occur. A medical practice with a staff consisting exclusively of registered nurses may not be as open to hiring medical assistants or licensed practical nurses as is a medical practice that already has a mix of medical assistants and registered nurses. A culture that only has physicians may not be open to hiring nonphysician providers.

Alternative Staffing Types

In addition to physicians and registered nurses, there are other skilled clinical professionals who can add significant value to the effectiveness of a medical practice. We explore a few of these professional roles next.

Nonphysician Providers

Nonphysician providers include nurse practitioners, physician assistants, and nurse midwives. Many practices have found that the patients value nonphysician providers highly because of their focus on patient education and the longer time that the nonphysician provider gives to the patient.

If hired, depending on state regulations, some nonphysician providers must work under the direction and supervision of a practicing, licensed physician. The supervising physician must have the appropriate training, experience, and competence to provide that supervision. In other states, nonphysician providers can work independently under their own licensure. It is best to always check with individual state licensure regulations.

The physician practice should determine whether a nonphysician provider would fit within the group and determine the types of duties and functions that he or she would perform. Many arrangements have failed because of lack of preparation for a nonphysician provider and a clear definition of the roles and duties of that position in advance.

Nonphysician providers can be accepted in one physician specialty or region of the United States but not accepted in another. The use of a nurse midwife in an OB/GYN practice is common, for example, except in regions of the United States where malpractice rates are high. The medical practice executive should determine whether the use of a nonphysician provider would work from many perspectives, including economic, operational, and strategic.

Part-Time Employees

Part-time employees can help the medical practice address changing practice needs. A part-time employee may be able to work flexible hours based on the patient load or have the time to cover employees who are on vacation, sick, or being trained. An employee in a part-time position may want to grow into a full-time position or may want the flexibility of fewer hours now and more hours later. These employees may fill either operational or clinical roles.

Outsourcing

Staffing costs or restrictions may require a medical practice to outsource certain functions. Common outsourced functions may be information technology services, housekeeping, maintenance, coding, and billing. These functions, as outsourced services, have their own set of deliverables and expectations. Outsourcing may be able to achieve greater cost savings than if those services were performed in house.

Staffing for Seasonality

Many practices have more full-time staff members than their patient base typically requires, so they can respond to high patient demand during seasonality changes, such as flu season or in practices located in winter or summer resort destinations. In addition, some practices use full-time *float* staff at their practice in case they are needed to cover vacation, sick leave, or family leave. These are high-cost staffing models.

There are a number of alternatives to this approach, including part-time on-call staff, part-time staff with variable hour arrangements, internal temporary employment pools or regional work pools, flexible scheduling, and cross-coverage arrangements that reduce staff FTE volumes and staffing costs. Other types of seasonal practice models are described as follows:

- **Early morning fast track clinics.** One of the seasonal practice models is to offer early morning fast track clinics involving walk-in for sick patients from 7:00 a.m. to 9:00 a.m. with no scheduled appointments during that time. Patients know they can be seen during this established walk-in clinic, thus minimizing both patient telephone calls to the practice and the physician on-call patient volume.

- **Enhanced weekend access.** Another method to support fluctuations in patient demand is to provide enhanced weekend access, thereby minimizing weekend physician on-call patient volume and high patient volumes on Monday mornings.
- **Expanded use of nonphysician providers.** Some practices have identified nonphysician providers to staff the work-in patients during high peak demands. This permits the physicians to maximally schedule their calendars with patients of higher acuity.
- **Walk-in facility.** A final example of a different practice model during fluctuations in patient demand is to devote additional resources to a current walk-in facility or to establish a walk-in facility during the high peak demand hours in order to enhance patient access.

These types of practice model variations during a seasonal fluctuation in patient demand tend to provide a more systematic approach to handling fluctuating patient volumes, rather than having each physician and associated staff members work harder and faster for prolonged periods of time.

Staff Recruitment

Finding the right number of staff members with the right mix of skills and compatible personalities is one of the biggest challenges a practice faces. Hires that are incompetent or a bad fit for their job can cause far-reaching consequences. Hiring and training employees is also expensive, so it is always of increased benefit to the practice to find the right employees from the beginning.

Recruiting from Inside the Organization

A medical practice that posts all positions internally prior to posting them externally has a *promotion-from-within* philosophy. This approach conveys to the workforce that the practice values hiring from within prior to considering external candidates. Usually a position is posted internally for several days and those candidates are interviewed prior to external candidates being considered. Some medical practices will post the position internally while concurrently posting the position for the external marketplace and, in the end, hire the best-qualified candidate.

Sometimes an internal referral is the best way to find a new staff person. An employee will usually refer someone who is thought to be a good worker because referring an unproductive worker will reflect poorly on that employee.

Recruiting External Candidates

There are many things to be aware of when recruiting externally, from nepotism to advertising strategies.

Hiring People with Close Relationships

Traditionally, nepotism has referred to hiring or advancing relatives solely because of their relationship with an employee, officer, or shareholder in an organization, without regard for their qualifications. Today, organizations are faced with a wider range of related people, including immediate family members, in-laws, step relatives, grandparents, and domestic partners.

The most stringent policies regarding close relationships in the workplace imposed by an organization prohibits hiring anyone with a close relation to an individual employed anywhere in the organization. Thus employment of a person at one location prevents a relative from being hired to work in any location. A less-restrictive policy bars employment only of employees with close relationships in the same facility, while a more liberal policy permits employment at the same site, but not within the same department or area. Finally, many policies prohibit people with close relationships from holding positions in which one person directly supervises another or has some influence over the other's pay, promotion, or work situation.

In carrying out relationship-in-the-workplace policies, employers must proceed cautiously when deciding whom to retain. If these decisions disparately affect females or older workers, employers are left open to discrimination claims. Employers are generally advised to let the individuals involved make the choice, and then, if possible, transfer to another department rather than terminate a person who decides to leave. It is important to make this decision on an objective and neutral basis.

Medical practices that have operated effectively without a policy regarding close relationships in the workplace may not need to implement one. Flexibility in the ability to hire closely related people may help recruit good candidates. Should a problem arise, a rule can be established with the precipitating incident providing the business necessity justification.

Advertising Strategy

Often, there are limited funds allocated to use for advertising job openings. The medical practice executive determines how that money will be allocated. Newspaper ads in local and regional papers, television commercials, Internet banners, magazine ads in professional journals, and direct mail are all examples of advertising strategies that medical practices have used to recruit new staff. The Internet and online job boards are becoming increasingly the first choice for posting open positions because of the ease and turnaround time to get the position posted.

Temporary Agencies

Temporary agencies can provide staff needed for a time-specific project or activity. They can also be resources for permanent employees. Hiring temporary agency staff allows a medical practice executive to determine whether a person possesses the necessary skills to perform the job on a continual basis and could fit within the organizational culture. Usually, if a company wants to hire a temporary agency worker, the agency charges a placement fee, which can be as much as 100 percent of the employee's first year's salary. Using temporary help is like having a working interview for the candidate.

Internet Job-Posting Services

With the growth of the Internet, jobs can now be advertised on the medical practice's Website and on Internet-based recruitment sites. An Internet search for a specific job or organization will bring up the job posting. This type of resource simplifies the job search for prospective candidates.

Search Firms

A search firm is a professional service provided to a medical practice to help attract, hire, and develop staff members who will hold jobs that are key to achieving the medical practice's goals and objectives. The service is paid for by the medical practice, not the hired person. Job candidates are presented to the medical group by the search firm based on employer-specified requirements.

Using a search firm can save the medical practice executive's time and money because identifying, qualifying, and reviewing potential candidates can be an expensive endeavor requiring tremendous effort.

Contingent vs. retained search firms. When a search firm is hired on a contingency basis, the firm will earn a fee only if a job candidate is hired and retained by the medical practice. A *headhunter* is a common term used for a contingent firm because most of the firm's effort is based on getting the potential candidate in front of the medical practice.

In contrast, hiring a retained search firm means that the medical practice has a signed contract with the firm to hire a candidate, and these two groups work exclusively with each other to find that person. Also, the search firm is paid in advance, in whole or in part, prior to the candidate being hired.

Regardless of the type of search firm contacted, the medical group and firm must correctly fit the potential job candidate with the skills needed for the job to achieve a satisfactory hiring outcome.

Community Placement Services

A community placement service helps link prospective job candidates to interested employers. These services may focus on working with students, new graduates, or displaced workers. The placement service is able to help the prospective job candidate develop a skill base, enhance the candidate's résumé, help him or her gain a better understanding of various job opportunities within the community, and develop networks and support systems of people who can provide letters of recommendation, references, and possible job options.

Employee Selection

The human resource department must be fair and consistent in its hiring practices. A person who starts working in the medical practice without following any of the procedures or policies may engender a complaint being filed by other coworkers. Common mistakes are failing to post a position internally, failing to complete an employment application, or letting a person begin employment without completing a drug screen or health physical. Even if the need to fill a position is urgent, it should never be done at the expense of following the process accepted by the medical practice. It is critical that the medical practice executive follow all legal practices and comply with all rules and regulations toward fair hiring practices.

There is a basic process for employee selection and customized applications, depending on the position.

Employment application form. The application is the same regardless of the position. An application should be completed prior to conducting any interviews. The application will ask for information such as demographics, education, work history, references, and criminal record. The potential employee will sign the application, indicating that the information is correct and authorizing a release to the medical practice to verify the information.

Equal employment opportunity (EEO) factors (e.g., advertising, recruiting, record-keeping). Careful records should be kept for any position being recruited. If a person later files a complaint against the medical practice caused by violation of EEO factors, the practice would want to demonstrate that its process was fair and consistent and complied with the law.

Interviewing (screening, behavior based). Screening interviews may be held on the telephone to determine the candidate's level of interest and skills for the position. Behavior-based interviews present the candidate with scenarios and ask how he or she would respond to those situations.

Phone interviews are a cost-effective and fast way to prescreen and filter job candidates. Phone interviews are effective for gathering information about past work experience and education before a personal interview is offered. This is also a way the interviewer can evaluate the speaking skills and phone etiquette of the applicant.

Job-specific interviews. Once a candidate has cleared the initial screening interview, he or she will typically be interviewed by the potential supervisor or a panel of people with whom the candidate potentially would work. This approach builds consensus from coworkers and allows them input into the process. Group interviews involve a panel of interviewers questioning several applicants scheduled closely together to determine who is the most qualified. These group interviews help interviewers evaluate applicants while the responses of previously interviewed candidates are still fresh in their minds. The interviewers should be carefully selected for each position. For example, the designated human resource professional responsible for recruitment should conduct the phone interview, and the direct manager or supervisor should interview the most highly qualified candidates. Employees who will work closely with the person ultimately hired can also conduct an interview with the best-qualified candidates.

Open-ended questions. Open-ended questions require more than just a "yes" or "no" answer. They encourage the candidate to discuss issues and share information about his or her background, experience, skills, and abilities, so that the employer can determine whether the candidate will be a good fit for the position.

Testing (written, performance). Some positions require a written or performance test to demonstrate competency in a job requirement. A medical secretary who is required to type 40 words a minute would take a typing test, or a file clerk would take a test showing the ability to file alphabetically and numerically.

Reference checks. A job candidate consenting to reference checks allows the employer to talk to other people about the candidate and ask questions without fear of being sued or risking legal action. Some previous employers will give out only limited information, including the employee's position title, starting and ending dates of employment, and rate of pay. Others will answer questions about a past employee's quality and quantity of work, time and attendance, customer service background, and whether the employer would rehire the employee. More information about this is included later in this chapter.

Criminal investigation and background checks. Questions on the job application ask the potential employee if he or she has ever been convicted of a misdemeanor or felony. An official background check is usually conducted after an employment offer and prior to the employee's first day of work to verify that the employee doesn't have any undisclosed criminal history. More information is included about this later in this chapter.

Offer of Employment

An offer of employment is usually made to the candidate with some time specified before a response is needed. If the position is accepted, a written confirmation is sent to the candidate confirming title, rate of pay, contingencies of employment, and start date. More information is included about this later in the chapter.

Health information and physical exams. An employment offer may be contingent on the person providing health information and passing a physical exam. There may be a preemployment drug physical to verify that the person is drug free. Failure to pass any of these tests may result in the employment offer being withdrawn. More information about this is included later in this chapter.

The Interview Process

The most commonly used selection technique is an interview, usually conducted on a one-to-one basis. The interview must also meet the standards of job-relatedness and nondiscrimination. Thus the same person should conduct interviews whenever possible, and the interviewer should ask a standard set of questions for each position.

Many employers believe that the interview is the quickest, safest, and fairest selection method, as well as being less costly and easier to validate than written tests. Using a variety of interviews is an excellent way to get a feel for the applicant's professional behavior. Many human resource professionals recommend that to maximize the probability of choosing the best possible employee, no applicant should be hired unless given two separate interviews.

The medical practice should provide interviewers with interview instructions and a list of appropriate and nondiscriminatory questions to ask. A variety of open-ended and hypothetical problem-solving questions should be asked. Avoid asking questions that the candidate can simply answer with only a "yes" or "no" answer.

Screening Potential Employees

Even if you know the person you plan to hire well, it is imperative to subject his or her application to a variety of screening tools that can alert you to problems that are easily hidden but may cause problems in the future.

Reference Checks

Reference checks involve verifying the information provided by an applicant as well as obtaining additional information about previous job performance. This information is used to evaluate a candidate's background and is a good indicator of future performance.

Thorough reference checks are strongly recommended in the healthcare industry. Many medical professionals have already demonstrated their proficiency through licensure, but the level and degree of competency and professionalism can only be determined by questioning former employers. Interviewers should always verify the status of the applicant's license. Furthermore, it is critical to verify the status of all credentials, including education and previous employment. It is not uncommon for applicants to lie on their résumés and employment applications about their credentials and other licenses. Detecting fraud at first glance can be difficult and exemplifies the importance of carefully reviewing résumés and applications before calling references. Follow these guidelines when reviewing résumés:

- Compare dates of graduation with dates of certification.
- Review all professional affiliations and identify those that do not quite fit or are misspelled.
- List all past employers the applicant reports are now out of business and supervisors who have left the organization. Many times this information is false and easy to verify.
- Be sensitive to gaps in employment; they can signal potential problems, including those previous jobs from which an applicant has been terminated or possibly when he or she spent time incarcerated.

Applicants who overstate their job qualifications may become unsatisfactory or harmful employees in the practice. As a warning, include a statement on your employment application form to the effect that résumé fraud results in immediate disqualification and/or termination. Proof of résumé fraud can be vital evidence in employer suits.

Before checking references, the employer needs a signed consent from the applicant, authorizing the employer to contact prior employers or educational institutions attended. This consent statement can be included in the application form. An example of a reference check consent form is presented in Exhibit 1.2. Your group practice may wish to consider using this language with necessary adaptations to make it reflect the practice's specific management philosophy, organizational needs, and staff size.

EXHIBIT 1.2

Reference Check Consent and Authorization Form[8]

This is a sample template of a Reference Check Consent form for conducting reference checks during the selection process. Check with your legal counsel to ensure compliance with federal and state laws.

REFERENCE CHECK CONSENT AND AUTHORIZATION FORM

I have applied for employment with *[Practice]* and have provided information about my previous employment. My signature below authorizes my former and current employers and references to release the contents of my employment record and to provide any additional information that may be necessary for my employment with *[Practice]*, whether the information is positive or negative.

I authorize *[Practice]* and its agents to investigate all statements made in my application for employment and to obtain any and all information concerning my former and/or current employment. This includes my job performance evaluations, wage history, disciplinary action(s), if any, and all other matters pertaining to my employment history. I knowingly and voluntarily release all former and current employers, references, and *[Practice]* from any and all liability of any kind, including but not limited to defamation, invasion of privacy, and breach of confidentiality arising from their giving or receiving information about my employment history, my academic credentials or qualifications, and my suitability for employment with *[Practice]*.

________________________________ ________________
Applicant Signature Date

____
Applicant Name (please print)

The other side of reference checks is providing information about current or former employees to other organizations. Many organizations have a policy to give only the essential information about a former employee, such as dates of employment, title of last job, and salary. Your group may need to emphasize interviews and trial periods, instead of former employers' accounts, to verify a person's competence.

The legal ramifications of reference checks have caused employers to be cautious; lawsuits have been filed because former employers did — or did not — provide reference information. Although employers generally enjoy a qualified privilege to references, unsubstantiated statements can destroy the privilege. The trend has been to share only information that was documented and can be easily defended.

Under certain circumstances, legal ramifications may also exist for an employer who does not exercise reasonable care in its selection of an employee if that employee later harms another in the course of the employment. Despite the reluctance of some employers to comment on former employees' performance, employers should still try to contact references and verify the information provided by the applicant.

Hiring employers should ask former employers about the dates of employment, title, duties and functions, quality of work, attendance and punctuality, ability to get along with coworkers, job performance, stated reason for leaving employment, and whether the former employers would rehire the individual. A written record should be kept of all reference checks and the information obtained. Additionally, all information obtained through reference checking should be held confidentially and should not be given to an applicant or referred to during the course of the interview and screening process. A sample reference checks policy is included in Exhibit 1.3.

Criminal Background Checks

Many states have laws requiring certain types of healthcare employers to perform criminal background or history checks. For example, employees who provide direct care to patients with physical or developmental disabilities or patients receiving inpatient, home, or hospice care are usually required to consent to a criminal background check. In some states, applicants who have been convicted of certain crimes, such as murder, assault, robbery, theft, and sex crime and drug-related convictions cannot be employed in these positions. Most state laws apply to

EXHIBIT 1.3

Reference Checks Policy[9]

This is an example of a reference checks policy. *This is a suggested policy for educational and illustrative purposes only. The particular laws of each state may differ, and this suggested general policy should not be implemented without considering applicable federal and state laws.*

REFERENCE CHECKS

Purpose: To establish and maintain guidelines for reference check requests.

Applies to: All *[Practice]* employees.

Policy: It is the policy of *[Practice]* to disclose only the date of hire, date of separation, and position held unless the former employee provides and signs an acceptable statement releasing *[Practice]* of any and all liability for the information provided. If such statement is signed, *[Practice]* may release the following documented information:

1. Positions held;
2. Date of hire;
3. Salary level;
4. Promotions;
5. Performance evaluations;
6. Attendance; and
7. Date of separation.

Any release of information will be in compliance with federal and state laws.

Approved by: Practice Administrator

Effective date: 1/1/20__

hospitals, nursing homes, home health agencies, hospices, community centers, and assisted-living centers.

The U.S. Equal Employment Opportunity Commission and some federal courts have taken the position that an employer cannot automatically reject an applicant because of a criminal conviction. You must evaluate whether and how the crime is related to the job sought. For example, a conviction for sexual assault is highly relevant for an applicant seeking a position with unsupervised patient contact. However, a conviction for failing to file income tax returns may have little relevance to a candidate's suitability for a maintenance or clerical position.

Generally employers have no obligation to tell applicants what they plan to look into as part of their consideration of an applicant. However, under federal law, criminal background and credit checks require prior disclosure to the applicant.

There are advantages to informing applicants that they may be subject to a criminal background check. First, applicants cannot claim that they did not know about the possibility of a criminal background check. Second, it may prevent applicants from lying on their application forms. Third, it may prevent some people from submitting their application because they do not want to undergo a criminal background check.

The depth of the investigation should be directly related to the vulnerability of the public if a dangerous person is put into the position. Minimal investigation is called for in the case of an outside groundskeeper, but staff positions that involve unsupervised contact with patients should receive substantial scrutiny. If a person is transferred into a patient-contact job, it is wise to run a more detailed background check.

An example of a consent statement for criminal background check form is provided in Exhibit 1.4. The practice may wish to adopt this statement with necessary adaptations to make it reflect your group's specific management philosophy, organizational needs, and staff size. Because state laws vary and may affect the legal requirements, the practice should also be familiar with these laws.

Credit Report Checks

Employers frequently check candidates' credit reports if the job duties involve handling money. If your medical practice will pull a candidate's credit report, the Fair Credit Reporting Act of 1970 requires that you

EXHIBIT 1.4

Criminal Background Check Authorization and Consent Form[10]

This is a sample template of a consent form for conducting criminal background checks during the selection process. Check with your legal counsel to ensure compliance with federal and state laws.

CRIMINAL BACKGROUND CHECK AUTHORIZATION AND CONSENT FORM

I understand that in considering my application for employment, *[Practice]* may conduct a comprehensive investigation of my qualifications. I understand this investigation may include, but is not limited to, a criminal background check, credit report, and references from past employers and other sources *[Practice]* deems appropriate.

I consent to any authorized representative of *[Practice]* to obtain information pertaining to my law enforcement record including, but not limited to, any record of charge, prosecution, or conviction for criminal offenses. I authorize each law enforcement agency to which this form is presented to release any results, upon request of the authorized requestors as described above.

I understand that these searches will be used to determine employment eligibility under *[Practice's]* employment policies. Therefore, I release and discharge *[Practice]* and its agents to the full extent of the law from any claims, losses, liabilities, or any other charge or complaint arising from retrieving and reporting this information.

I hereby certify that the information provided on this Criminal Background Check Authorization and Consent Form is true, correct, and complete. I understand that any information which is proven to be incorrect or incomplete may disqualify me from further consideration for employment and may result in my dismissal if discovered at a later date.

Applicant Signature	**Date**

Printed Name (Last, first, MI)			**Maiden Name**
Other Names Used (Last, first, MI)			
Current Address (Street number and name)		**Apt. #**	**Date of Birth** (Month/day/year)
City	**State**	**Zip Code**	**Social Security #**
Driver's License #	**State Issued**	**Expiration Date**	☐ **Male** ☐ **Female**

disclose that you may use credit report findings in the selection process prior to pulling the report. The Federal Trade Commission, which enforces the law, requires a stand-alone disclosure and authorization form to be completed by each applicant. A sample credit report authorization and consent form is provided in Exhibit 1.5. In addition, the employer must provide candidates a copy of the report, inform them which consumer reporting company was used, and state their rights under the Fair Credit Reporting Act if the results eliminate them from the selection process.

Negligent Hiring

Negligent hiring is a legal theory that says an employer who fails to take reasonable precautions to ensure that employees will not harm a coworker can be held liable. With disturbing and increasing frequency, disgruntled employees are taking out their anger and frustration on coworkers or customers (i.e., patients). Lawsuits can then claim that the employer did not do an adequate job of investigating the employee's background before hiring. The injured party argues that if the employer had done an adequate investigation, it would have learned of the employee's violent tendencies. Thus the employer's negligence resulted in harm that was foreseeable.

There are steps you can take to substantially reduce your medical practice's exposure to claims of negligent hiring, while also preventing complaints of discrimination, breach of confidentiality, and defamation:

1. Use an application form that has been reviewed by legal counsel.
2. Conduct a telephone screening interview with qualified candidates to review their résumés, application forms, and past work experiences. Ask about any lapses in employment history.
3. Interview qualified candidates face to face in private.
4. Discuss and have the applicant sign the reference check consent form and the criminal background and credit history consent form.
5. If the applicant's duties will require driving, obtain proof of a valid driver's license, and, in some circumstances, discuss and have the applicant sign a driving record consent form.

EXHIBIT 1.5

Credit Report Authorization and Consent Form[11]

This is a sample template of a consent form for authorization to pull an applicant's credit report during the selection process. Check with your legal counsel to ensure compliance with federal and state laws.

CREDIT REPORT AUTHORIZATION AND CONSENT FORM

I understand that in considering my application for employment, *[Practice]* may conduct a comprehensive investigation of my qualifications. I understand that this investigation may include, but is not limited to, a criminal background check, credit report, and references from past employers and other sources *[Practice]* deems appropriate.

I hereby authorize and consent for *[Practice's]* procurement of a consumer credit report. I understand that, pursuant to the federal Fair Credit Reporting Act, *[Practice]* will provide me with a copy of any such report if the information contained in such report is, in any way, to be used in making a decision regarding my fitness for employment with *[Practice]*. I further understand that such report will be made available to me prior to any such decision being made, along with the name and address of the reporting agency that produced the report.

Applicant Signature	**Date**

Printed Name (Last, first, MI)	**Maiden Name**
Other Names Used (Last, first, MI)	

Current Address (Street number and name)		**Apt. #**	**Date of Birth** (Month/day/year)
City	**State**	**Zip Code**	**Social Security #**
□ **Male** □ **Female**			

6. Contact the applicant's references to verify truthfulness on employment history.
7. Confirm educational and licensure credentials provided by applicant.
8. Order a criminal background check and/or the applicant's driving record if necessary.

The more information the practice seeks and the more data obtained about an applicant, the better prepared you are to make hiring decisions. In conducting interviews, criminal background checks, and other investigative efforts, it is imperative that you first understand what the applicable federal and state laws require, permit, and prohibit. Check with your legal counsel about these issues.

Employment Offers

Once your medical practice has selected the most qualified candidate for a position, the offer of employment is made. Offers can be made either verbally or in writing. Remind interviewers that verbal representations may result in unintended contractual commitments for the practice. Verbal offers should always be followed up with a written offer of employment. Written correspondence with applicants should be carefully reviewed by your legal counsel to ensure that representations do not result in unwanted contractual obligations.

The practice is advised to develop a standard offer letter, reviewed by your legal counsel, to avoid making unintended promises regarding employment; the letter should include an employment-at-will clause. Avoid any definitive promises by the practice. The salary should be framed in the shortest possible time period, such as hourly wage or monthly salary. The letter should also state a time limit for acceptance of the offer and should include any preemployment responsibilities of the applicant. Under the ADA, the practice may offer a job on the condition of satisfactory results of post-offer medical exams or drug tests.

Post-Offer Health Examinations

To decrease the possibility of discrimination in the hiring process, the ADA prohibits employers from making preemployment inquiries about a candidate's disabilities.[12] An employer may only ask whether an applicant can perform the job functions with or without reasonable accommodation. Even if the applicant volunteers information about a disability, the employer should only discuss the individual's ability to perform the essential functions of the job.

Requiring medical examinations of applicants is restricted by the ADA.[13] Employers may require an applicant to submit to a medical examination only after conditionally offering the applicant a job. It is not sufficient for ADA compliance for the employer to simply narrow down the selection to the final applicants. Although the offer can be contingent on a satisfactory health examination, a subsequent withdrawal of the offer based on the examination results must be related to an employee's ability to perform the job. Only results of such examination that indicate the person is unable to perform the essential functions of the position may be used to deny employment to the applicant. An employer may also withdraw an offer if the applicant's disability poses a direct threat to the applicant or others in the workplace, and the threat cannot be eliminated by reasonable accommodation.

Post-offer medical examinations must be required for all candidates in the same job category to whom an employer makes offers. Employers who use medical examinations must treat the results as confidential medical records. The results may only be released to certain individuals in limited circumstances, as indicated by law.

Health examinations of current employees may only be conducted if they are job related and necessary to the operation of the business. For example, safety concerns or a sudden unexplained decrease in job performance might warrant a medical examination of an employee. The examination may not include tests or inquiries that are not related to the employee's ability to perform the job. Employers may also conduct examinations pursuant to an employee health program, but only if participation is voluntary and the results are kept confidential.

The underlying purpose of requiring health examinations is to obtain information on health status. Along with determining whether the applicant is in adequate physical condition to perform the job functions, health examinations can protect the employer from invalid workers' compensation claims in cases where injuries or illness were present when an employee was hired.

Medical practices may choose to use health histories, physical exams, or both, depending on the health status of the applicant and the physical requirements of the position. In healthcare organizations, health screening is particularly relevant for employees directly involved with hands-on patient care. To ensure employees do not have a health condition that jeopardizes patients' health, require all such caregivers to complete a health screening questionnaire signed by their physician as soon as possible after hire.

Your medical practice may also choose to use a simple immunization history form that does not need to be signed by a physician. Health histories help to evaluate the current medical, physical, and mental condition of an employee or applicant to determine overall job suitability. If the person's health history reveals any serious medical, physical, or mental problems that might interfere with successful and safe job performance, the medical practice has the right to request a medical examination to determine the current medical status and extent of previous injuries, diseases including HIV and AIDS, or handicaps. For example, if the candidate has a history of back problems and applies for a licensed practical nurse position, which requires heavy lifting of as much as 100 pounds, the medical practice would want a further detailed medical evaluation of the applicant's ability to lift.

Health examinations also help employers determine, with the help of a physician, if a disabled applicant can perform the essential functions of a job with or without reasonable accommodations, and what accommodations are necessary.

A sample of a policy for health examinations is provided in Exhibit 1.6. Because state laws vary and may affect the legal requirements, the practice should consult its legal counsel and become familiar with these laws.

Post-Offer Drug Testing

Under the ADA, a test to detect the illegal use of drugs is not considered a medical examination. Thus employers may administer drug tests to applicants to discover illegal use of drugs. Employers may also prohibit employees from being under the influence of alcohol, illegal drugs such as cocaine and heroin, and the illegal use of prescription drugs in the workplace.

EXHIBIT 1.6

Health Examinations Policy[14]

This is an example of a health examinations policy. *This is a suggested policy for educational and illustrative purposes only. The particular laws of each state may differ, and this suggested general policy should not be implemented without considering applicable federal and state laws.*

HEALTH EXAMINATIONS

Purpose: To establish and maintain guidelines for health examinations.

Applies to: All *[Practice]* employees.

Policy: The policy of *[Practice]* is to require its employees to have a health examination under the circumstances outlined below.

Procedures:

1. After a conditional job offer, all individuals are required to satisfactorily complete a health examination form and have it signed by their physician as soon as possible after hire. Some health examinations may be required to include a physician's report and medical records when there is a concern about the person's ability to perform the job.
2. Management reserves the right to request that an employee have a physical examination at any time when the health and safety of the employee or patients is in question.
3. Health and physical examinations administered at the request of management are paid for by the group.
4. Any medical examinations paid for by *[Practice]* are the group's property and treated as confidential.
5. When *[Practice]* requires a physician's report concerning an illness suffered by an employee, the examination is at *[Practice's]* expense and performed by a physician selected by the group. Employees who are not satisfied with the physician's report may submit one from a physician of their own choice and at their own expense. *[Practice's]* physician evaluates results of this examination and makes a final determination.
6. Employees returning from sick leave may be required to have a physical examination, limited to the condition causing the absence, to determine their capability to satisfactorily perform their regular job duties.
7. Employees who are exposed to any occupational health hazard, such as toxic materials, fumes, or nuclear radiation, are required to have a physical examination, limited to the substances to which employees are exposed. The physician determines whether exposed employees require medical treatment and/or whether they may be permitted to continue their jobs.

Approved by: Practice Administrator

Effective date: 1/1/20__

An employee or applicant found to be currently using drugs in an illegal manner is not protected as a qualified individual with a disability. An employer may make employment decisions on the basis of current illegal drug use. Employers should be careful, however, to ensure that the drug test results they rely on are accurate.

Although the ADA does not prohibit drug testing of applicants, employers should be aware that drug test results showing use of a particular drug can indicate the existence of a disability. The disability could then be considered known, and a duty to reasonably accommodate it might arise. Employers who choose to use drug tests should test all applicants as a condition of employment.

Conclusion

An effective hiring process is critical to the success of a medical practice. The process ranges from analyzing skill needs and staffing requirements through the identification of potential personnel, implementation of the hiring process itself, and documentation of the process to meet regulatory requirements.

Notes

1. *MGMA Performance and Practices of Successful Medical Groups* (Englewood, CO: Medical Group Management Association, 2014).
2. *MGMA Performance and Practices of Successful Medical Groups.*
3. Jan Reid, "Does Staff Have 'Skin in the Game'? If They Do, Your Practice Wins." *MGMA Connexion* 12, no. 2 (2012): 13–14.
4. *MGMA Performance and Practices of Successful Medical Groups.*
5. Deborah L. Walker and David N. Gans, *Rightsizing; Appropriate Staffing for Your Medical Practice* (Englewood, CO: Medical Group Management Association, 2003).
6. Keegan, D.W. *Innovative Staffing for the Medical Practice* (Englewood, CO: Medical Group Management Association, 2011); MGMA DataDive cost and revenue modules, 2003–2015, www.mgma.com/industry-data/survey-reports/mgma-datadive-online-benchmarking-with-mgma-surveys
7. *MGMA Physician Compensation and Production Survey: 2014 Report Based on 2013 Data* (Englewood, CO: Medical Group Management Association, 2014).

8. Source: Courtney Price, *HR Policies and Procedures: Manual for Medical Practices*, 5th ed. (Englewood, CO: Medical Group Management Association, 2014). Reprinted with permission.
9. Source: Price, *HR Policies and Procedures*. Reprinted with permission.
10. Source: Price, *HR Policies and Procedures*. Reprinted with permission.
11. Source: Price, *HR Policies and Procedures*. Reprinted with permission.
12. "ADA Enforcement Guidance: Preemployment Disability-Related Questions and Medical Examinations," U.S. Equal Employment Opportunity Commission, Oct. 10, 1995, modified July 6, 2000, www.eeoc.gov/policy/docs/medfin5.pdf.
13. "ADA Enforcement Guidance."
14. Source: Price, *HR Policies and Procedures*. Reprinted with permission.

Chapter 2

Directing and Managing Retention of Clinical and Nonclinical Staff

Managing the retention of staff is an ongoing responsibility for any medical practice administrator. Retention is more than just keeping the employees you have; it includes oversight of conflict resolution, team development, personnel record-keeping, and other day-to-day operational tasks. The key knowledge and skills necessary to manage retention are:

- Knowledge of labor relations;
- Managing employee motivation and teamwork to obtain high performance;
- Maintaining a healthy workplace environment, including conflict resolution process and grievance procedure;
- Providing access to an employee assistance program; and
- Keeping personnel records.

Retention and Motivation

The ability to retain and motivate your most talented employees is directly related to the success of your group practice. The cost of recruiting and training new employees is easily double that of a departing employee's salary. Because of the shortages of qualified applicants in many healthcare fields, retaining your top talent is crucial to your group's success.

Your group practice should establish a culture that promotes employee involvement and encourages top talent to stay with the practice for the long run. Your goal should be to become an employer of choice in your community.

Many talented employees seek to work for a high-performance and well-run group practice. They want an opportunity to grow within their jobs, increase their responsibilities, and obtain promotions. Top talent wants competitive pay and fringe benefits based on performance- and merit-based reward systems.

Motivation starts at the top of your group practice. Motivated managers have motivated employees. Management should be proactive in anticipating any dissatisfaction in their top employees. To motivate and retain your employees, your group practice should find out what employees want, and then determine how to give it to them or how they can earn it. Elements for retaining and motivating top talent include:

- Employee engagement;
- Continuing education; and
- Competitive rewards and incentives.

Employee Engagement

Organizations with engaged employees are successful, productive, and cost-effective. Labor is the largest expense in most group practices. Finding a way to retain and motivate your top employees increases productivity and profitability. Gallup's 2013 *State of the American Workforce* report says that businesses in the top 25 percent of employee engagement had less turnover and significantly higher profitability, revenues, and percentages of customer loyalty.[1] The correlation between employee engagement and productivity is strong.

Engagement begins by providing your employees with everything and anything, within reason, that they need to do their jobs and be successful. Employees should have all the materials they need within an arm's reach to be as productive as possible. Your supervisors should be sure that new hires have the necessary resources to start working in their new positions immediately and to continue their work throughout the year.

Your group practice should clearly communicate to all employees what is expected of them, what the vision of the group practice is, what the group practice values, and how the group practice measures success. Employees cannot be engaged or productive if they do not know what is expected from them and how they will be evaluated. Your group practice's vision should be shared by all top-level managers, and you should encourage your employees to help the group practice achieve its vision.

Employees become motivated and engaged when the rewards they earn truly mean something. Getting to know each of your employee's personality and behavioral traits and providing employee-specific rewards will increase productivity, engagement, motivation, and retention.

Many people want to feel that their skills are being used to the optimal level in their jobs. Managers should be aware of which employees have what skills and place them in job functions that optimize those skills. Employees should also be given responsibilities that they find challenging but not overly stressful.

Special Considerations for Retaining Physicians

Managing expectations is one of the keys to successful retention. To do so involves fostering two-way communication, implementing a physician recognition program, and providing forums to review opportunities.

Physician supervisors should schedule regular individual and group meetings with new doctors to answer questions, discuss concerns, and provide feedback to keep morale high. Holding regional or system-wide forums twice a year is a good way to meet with the group and encourage two-way communication. Smaller practices should get all physicians and nonphysician providers together to discuss issues.

Practices and physicians must develop and maintain common expectations of the group's mission, values, and goals to work effectively as a team. In the past this understanding could be unwritten. With today's pressures and complexities, it is a good idea to write down the group's common mission, values, and expectations. Review them periodically to see if any adjustments are necessary. Successful groups maintain:

- A written statement of mission and values;
- Measurable quality and business goals;
- Periodic measurements and reviews of the practice's progress; and
- Agreed-on expectations among physicians.[2]

Integrating the Culture

A physician orientation program that embodies practice culture can assist physician retention by accelerating the integration process for new hires. The practice culture is a system of shared beliefs, values, and behaviors within an organization. Indicators that a practice exhibits cultural integration include physicians who are:

- Willing to delegate authority and give up individual autonomy;
- Able to work collaboratively to solve problems;
- Committed and/or willing to follow group goals and directives;
- Accepting of consolidation of practices and economies of scale;
- Willing to share income, expense, and/or governance;
- Focused on the long term and the short term; and
- Willing to deal with problems of other group physicians.[3]

Cultural integration should also include communicating the governance structure. Typically, a practice elects a small-sized board or executive committee, with clear differentiation between the roles of the board (making policies) and management (implementing policies).

Finally, strong leadership — both physician and administrative — must exist for a successful cultural integration. New physicians must be given appropriate accountabilities to ensure that they understand their roles and responsibilities.[4]

Teambuilding Programs

Teambuilding training programs accompanied with skill-based exercises can be used to improve working relationships among coworkers, supervisors, and managers. By developing your staff's interpersonal skills, communication tends to flow more freely and effectively across and among departmental boundaries.

Often these workshops uncover internal working issues and misunderstandings among the employees, which result in less efficient patient care. Offering these types of workshops help employees confront these small dissatisfactions among staff members. It is not unusual for practices to experience disconnect among departments, management, and staff. Teambuilding workshops can enhance and build stronger camaraderie and team spirit. Effective teams work together more efficiently and result in higher patient satisfaction. Employees enjoy the opportunity to expand and develop their skills, which results in a more motivated, engaged, and effective workforce.

Continuing Education

Providing continuing education opportunities adds to an employee's job satisfaction. Continuing education can be used to train your most talented employees to become the next generation of managers, or it can be used as a reward incentive. Continuing education is a must for many of your employees to keep their technical skills current. However, offering continuing education programs to noncertified or nonlicensed employees is a good practice for enhancing motivation and retention.

Understanding Generational Differences

It is obvious that people of different ages are often looking for different things in the workplace, but generational preferences and differences are rarely considered when it comes to staff retention. The four generational groups currently in the workforce are:

1. **World War II:** Those born prior to the Second World War and those whose earliest memories and influences are associated with the Great Depression and World War II;
2. **Baby boomers:** Those born between 1940 and 1960 and reared in the pro-child era of extreme optimism, opportunity, and progress;
3. **Generation Xers:** Those born after the baby boom (between 1960 and 1980) who came of age deep in the shadow of the boomers and in an anti-child environment; and
4. **Millennials:** Those born after 1980 and reared during a time when children were celebrated and heroes existed.

Exhibit 2.1 shows how the different generations see the world.

EXHIBIT 2.1

Generational Viewpoint Differences[5]

How each generation sees the world ...

	World War II	Baby Boomers	Generation Xers	Millennials
Outlook	Practical	Optimistic	Skeptical	Hopeful
Work ethic	Dedicated	Driven	Balanced	Determined
View of authority	Respectful	Love/Hate	Unimpressed	Polite
Leadership by	Hierarchy	Consensus	Competence	Pulling together
Relationships	Personal sacrifice	Personal gratification	Reluctant to commit	Inclusive
Turnoffs	Vulgarity	Political incorrectness	Cliché, hype	Promiscuity
Perspective	Civic minded	Team oriented	Self-reliant	Civic minded

Common Traits of All Generations

While it is easy to focus on the differences among the generations, there are many similarities as well, and successful practices create work environments that support them. Research conducted by the Center for Creative Leadership[6] found interesting similarities among employees regardless of generation:

- Work is a vehicle for personal fulfillment and satisfaction, not just a paycheck;
- Workplace culture is very important;
- Ninety-one percent of employees agree that being trusted to get the job done is the number one factor defining job satisfaction;
- Eighty-six percent of employees say they need to feel valued by their employer to be happy at work;
- More than 6 of 10 employees want career planning;
- Sixty-seven percent seek flexibility in workplace schedules; and
- All generations define success as finding a company they can stay with for a long time.

Retaining Generation X and Millennial Physicians

It's imperative that healthcare organizations create recruitment and retention strategies designed with the Generation X and millennial physicians in mind. These younger physicians are less willing to pay their dues to an organization or take on additional responsibilities without promises of higher compensation or partnership. They demand flex time and seek a nonstressful work–life balance. Married male physicians are expecting more family involvement than previous generations. Many Generation X and millennial physicians want to continuously develop skills so they can have options and opportunities to move to other organizations if a better situation presents itself.

Dissatisfaction with their choice of medical career is evident in recent statistics: One in four newly trained physicians would still choose another field if they could. The first three years of practice are critical for new physicians and hold the greatest likelihood for turnover. Poor cultural fit with the practice and the community as well as a desire to be near family members were most frequently mentioned when asked the reasons for the turnover.

To attract and retain young physicians, employers need to provide:[7]

- A values-driven, relationship-oriented culture;
- Strong orientation and mentoring programs, which offer continuing development of marketable, manageable skill sets;
- Flexibility in scheduling with an emphasis on work–life balance;
- Prompt attention during the recruitment phase and when employed;
- Expeditious response to calls, e-mails, and text messages;
- Formal development of a physician retention program with clear expectations about compensation and long-term potential before the physician start date;
- Development of interpersonal connections with new physician and peers from the start date through the initial 90 days;
- Regular feedback and performance reviews (a very important retention factor for physicians after the initial 90 days);
- Partnership and ownership opportunities; and
- Spouse relocation assistance during recruitment process.

Six Principles for Successfully Mixing Generations

The following six principles can be implemented for mixing the generations successfully.[8]

1. **Initiate conversations about generations.** We often make judgments about each other without realizing those judgments are generational in nature. And we tend to keep those judgments under the table. When we get them out in the open, the issues become less personalized and more generalized. They become easier — and sometimes fun — to talk about.
2. **Ask people about their needs and preferences.** Out of the best intentions, we often project our preferences onto others. The only way to know for certain what someone else's needs and preferences are is to ask!
3. **Offer options.** Working successfully with a mix of generations means being flexible and offering as many choices as possible to suit the needs and preferences of a diverse workforce.
4. **Personalize your style.** Be flexible. Practice the Titanium Rule: Learn about preferences of others on your team and find creative ways to meet their expectations.
5. **Build on strengths.** The best mixed-generation work teams recognize the unique strengths of each individual. Urge people who are different to become more of who they already are, rather than trying to blend in with the rest of the team.
6. **Pursue different perspectives.** Many work teams would tell you that they tolerate differences, but the mixed-generation ones that truly succeed go far beyond tolerance. Choose people with varied backgrounds and perspectives to work together on projects.

Conflict Resolution

Establishing effective employee relations and appropriate conflict resolution programs are necessary to work toward common goals. The word *team* is overused in healthcare: It conveys the expectation that everyone will work together to accomplish a common purpose. Often, employees and departments experience conflicts that thwart the attainment of high performance. When this happens, the supervisor needs to get involved and talk with the employees one on one or in groups to identify the problems and determine a resolution.

There are sobering statistics with regard to costs from workplace conflicts and litigation. According to Enterprise Florida, the official economic development organization of the state of Florida:[9]

- Six out of 10 employers have faced an employee lawsuit;
- An average out-of-court settlement is $40,000;
- Ten percent of wrongful termination and discrimination cases result in a $1,000,000 settlement;
- Sixty-seven percent are ruled in the plaintiff's favor when taken to litigation.

Sometimes an objective third party may need to get involved if issues are plagued with cultural or historical resistance, or if the process of change isn't supported by the physicians. A third party may also need to get involved if the conflict is between the employee and supervisor. Differences in problem-solving styles, information processing, and communication can create conflicts that, if not resolved soon after identification, may lead to disastrous consequences.

Managing Conflict

When conflict arises, there are some basic actions you can take to manage conflict productively. Practice these actions yourself and encourage your team to use them:

- **Focus on the problem, not the person.** This is a critical step in managing conflict. By looking primarily at the problem, it helps to take defensiveness and emotions out of the process. Look at the problem, jointly decide alternative solutions to solve the problem, then select the best solution and implement it.
- **Maintain the self-confidence and self-esteem of both the other person and yourself.** Focus on keeping the self-confidence and self-esteem of both parties intact. If either you or the other person becomes defensive during this process, then you will have two problems to deal with — the initial problem as well as the problem of the other person's defensiveness.

- **Maintain a positive and constructive relationship.** Focus on doing all that you can to build and maintain positive and constructive relationships.

With many of our colleagues, we will have ongoing relationships and dealings for years to come. As the old saying goes, "It's easy to win the battle and lose the war." Work to create win–win relationships with all the people in your life.

Conflict Resolution Personnel Policy

The personnel policy should state which representative will resolve the conflict. It may be the human resource department representative, the medical practice executive, an employee and labor relations consultant, or, if the practice is unionized, the union steward. This person will meet with the employee, supervisor, or both, as is appropriate to the chain of command, to help in resolving their differences. This representative can provide advice on matters of policy interpretation, rights of management and employees, and information on the formal grievance process.

The personnel policy may have a statement on protection against retaliation of employees for exercising their rights under the arbitration process. There may be time limits on the process to facilitate speedy resolution of the problem while providing appropriate time to collect, prepare, and present information. For example, if the employee fails to follow the time limits, the issue may be deemed to be resolved to the employee's satisfaction. If the medical practice fails to follow specific time limits, the employee may take the complaint to a higher level of resolution. Personnel policies should reflect current federal, state, and local employment laws.

Policy Interpretation for Grievance Procedures

For all disciplinary action, policy interpretation is a human resource department responsibility. The disciplinary action or progressive discipline process is meant to give appropriate feedback to the employee in a formal way. This constructive feedback for desired results is meant to provide the employee with measurable accomplishments, instill individual accountability and responsibility, and facilitate the desired behavior. The supervisor can serve as a mentor, coach, and facilitator of the process and help the employee understand the desired results.

If the communication requires multiple areas of behavior change, the supervisor may choose to give the employee a performance improvement plan (PIP). This tool focuses on below-average or substandard performance and provides an action plan for needed change. The plan is time specific and allows the employee to receive periodic feedback. For example, an employee may receive a PIP for inappropriate interactions with patients. The PIP would provide the employee with customer service training and weekly feedback sessions between the supervisor and employee on improvement in the desired area. Failure to achieve desired results can lead to additional disciplinary action up to and including termination. The PIP's intent is to help the employee be successful and shepherd the process.

Mediation

Mediation allows the employer and employee to troubleshoot issues and reestablish positive relations. It allows problems to be dealt with promptly and provides an opportunity to address a problem before it escalates into an unworkable issue.

Mediation usually moves away from blame or judgment to allow a win–win situation instead of a win–lose situation. The two parties, not the mediator, control the situation and the outcome.

Mediation can be used prior to a formal grievance process, such as arbitration. Using mediation, however, does not waive one's right to use a formal grievance process if the parties cannot reach a satisfactory outcome through mediation.

In mediation, a professional mediator contacts the two parties involved and seeks to achieve agreement. Usually, each party meets individually with a mediator first to identify and discuss the concerns. The mediator keeps all information from these sessions confidential. Then the mediator brings the two parties together to discuss the concerns, and works toward a win–win outcome. Sometimes a second session may be required, depending on the complexity of the issue.

If the two parties reach an agreement, the mediator works with them to create a written agreement, listing the specific components of the agreement, which both parties sign. Usually these agreements do not change existing medical practice policies or union contracts.

Arbitration

Nonbinding arbitration is a way of avoiding disputes because it provides a written guide on the practice used in employee grievances. The purpose of the arbitration policy is to establish a procedure for the fair, orderly, and speedy resolution of disputes that sometimes arise between management and employees. The policy states to whom it applies (e.g., all members, unclassified employees) and how the policy is used. An employee may use the procedure to review an alleged violation of the medical practice's policy or rules pertaining to employment.

Nonbinding vs. Binding Arbitration

In a nonbinding arbitration process, two parties give a dispute to a neutral person to determine an advisory or nonbinding decision, meaning that neither party is required to accept the opinion. In the process, the two groups have input into the selection of the person arbitrating. Nonbinding arbitration is used when the parties want a quick dispute resolution, prefer a third-party decision maker, and want more control over the decision-making process if the dispute is not resolved.

In binding arbitration, both parties present a dispute to an impartial arbitrator to determine a binding decision. The parties have the ability to decide who serves as the arbitrator. Binding arbitration is appropriate when the parties want a neutral third party to decide the outcome of the dispute and avoid a formal trial. The parties do not retain control over how their dispute is resolved and cannot appeal the arbitrator's decision.

Employee Grievance Procedures[10]

When an employee has a grievance against the practice, initially there should be an attempt at an informal resolution of complaints. Regular communication between the practice managers and employees reduces the need for a more formal review and is in the mutual best interest of the medical practice and employees. Written resource materials, handouts, and guides should always be available to help management communicate information with employees.

An employee who has a work-related problem should bring it to the medical practice executive's attention with the intent of resolving the problem. In a timely manner, management should discuss the concern with the employee with an effort to resolve the issue. If informal attempts at resolution are not satisfactory, employees may use a formal grievance process.

Listening to employees is key to ensuring excellent performance. Active listening helps identify whether any issues or concerns are preventing the employee from performing the expected job duties. Early identification of problems can avoid serious problems later. If, through active listening, a supervisor recognizes that a problem exists that requires a higher level of problem solving or counseling, the supervisor needs to recognize his or her limitations and refer the employee to either the human resource department or, if offered, an employee assistance program (EAP) to help the employee sort through personal issues that are inhibiting acceptable performance levels.

Employee Assistance Program

In today's changing workplace environment, the medical practice executive is expected to provide more services with fewer dollars. Employees are expected to do more tasks and handle stressful situations professionally. This stress may cause worry, confusion, doubt, and even sickness. Dealing with prolonged stress may cause fatigue, depression, anger, and anxiety, which may lead to defensiveness, inappropriate behavior, and coworker conflict.

Although some worry and anxiety is normal, sometimes these emotions can become problematic and affect employee productivity, lower employee morale, and foster poor outcomes. An EAP helps the employee stay on track and provides coping mechanisms to perform better in a state of uncertainty.

An EAP is a medical practice resource that uses a comprehensive program of counseling services for employees and/or their dependents to help improve employee and workplace effectiveness. It provides confidential, third-party counseling, and work–life balancing services to employees in an off-site setting, and its effectiveness is through its efforts toward prevention, identification, and resolution of employee personal problems that affect employee productivity.

EAP services may be provided by the employer's own EAP or through an external agency. The EAP is not a mandated employee benefit, yet it can be very beneficial in reducing employee risk, cutting costs for recruitment of new employees, and improving employee productivity. Employees may use an EAP for counseling or further referrals for financial counseling (e.g., bankruptcy, money management, gambling), family issues (e.g., death, divorce, separation), domestic violence (e.g., spousal or child abuse), alcohol and substance abuse, mental health issues (e.g., depression, suicidal ideation, phobias), and family law (e.g., adoption, custody, restraining orders). The medical practice executive may use an EAP to help employees better address issues that affect poor performance, provide an on-site counselor in case of a traumatic event (e.g., employee death), or provide on-site training to handle employee issues more effectively.

An EAP may be needed by an employee as a further condition of employment. If the employer believes that the employee cannot continue working in the medical practice without EAP services, then it becomes a mandatory referral. However, most EAP services are sought by the employee voluntarily. EAP services are usually available to all part-time and full-time employees, regardless of employment position.

Open Door Policy

Practices should encourage employees to bring forward any concerns or complaints they may have regarding their employment and provide guidelines for them to do so. The practice's open door policy should be in the employee handbook and also included in employee onboarding training, as well as in any training updates. The policy should indicate specifically whom employees should complain to and in what order. Generally, open door policies direct employees to first raise any concerns with their managers, if appropriate. If that is not appropriate, or if the employee is not satisfied with the outcome, then the policy may direct the employee to address his or her concern with someone in an upper level management position.

Policies may have three or more levels of personnel of progressively higher levels of authority for an employee to potentially approach. Finally, the policy should clarify that any concerns relating to unlawful discrimination or harassment should be addressed through the specific complaint procedure set forth in the discrimination and harassment policy.

Whistleblowing

Whistleblowing is when an employee or former employee raises concerns about illegal behavior. Whistleblowing is different from other types of complaints. Generally, non-whistleblowing complaints are when an employee raises concerns about the way in which the employer has acted in relation to his or her personal performance or conduct. Whistleblowing is focused on raising concerns about misconduct and/or unethical or illegal behavior or activities occurring in an organization. Although the most famous whistleblowing cases were reported to regulators or other government officials, whistleblowing has also occurred internally in medical practices.

Medical practices should have a culture of openness and establish a procedure for reporting concerns especially where patient safety may be at risk or when other concerns surface, such as acts of substance abuse, drug diverting, theft, inappropriate relationships, legal ethics, and/or safety violations. Employers should adopt an honest and transparent approach so employees feel comfortable in raising concerns internally to promote a culture of openness.

Physician practices are required to have compliance programs. As part of the compliance program, and to achieve open lines of communication, practices should establish a simple procedure for reporting concerns by using telephone hotlines or other anonymous reporting methods as well as nonretaliation policies protecting whistleblowers who report violations in good faith.

One effective way to do this is to designate a corporate compliance officer and create a reporting process that allows the employee an open, anonymous, and protected method of communication with the compliance officer. The corporate compliance officer should be a high-level person who reports directly to the highest governing authority, typically the board of directors. This person should provide the governing body periodic updates on the effectiveness of the compliance program.

There are federal and state laws that offer different types of whistleblower protection according to the subject matter of the complaint, and the type and size of employer. Medical practices should be aware that these laws aim to protect the whistleblower's rights, including protection against retaliation. The practice should have a policy addressing how whistleblowers may report misconduct and how their rights will be protected. Regardless of the practice's size, the whistleblower policy is a critical tool for the practice with respect to patient safety, correcting or improving systems and practices, and promoting employee morale, as well as a positive culture and image of the practice in the community.

Unions

The Wagner Act of 1935, otherwise known as the National Labor Relations Act (NLRA), was passed to protect employees' rights to unionize. The National Labor Relations Board (NLRB) was created to implement and enforce the NLRA. Numerous labor laws are currently in place; however, the Wagner Act marked the federal government's initial support for unionization and collective bargaining. The NLRB conducts elections to determine whether employees want union representation and also examines unfair labor practices by employers and unions. The NLRA guarantees employees the right to self-organize, choose representation, and bargain collectively.

The NLRB must also make sure that employers do not discriminate against union members. Labor laws allow employees the right to unionize and to participate in strikes, picketing, and lockouts to have their demands met. Employee areas for consideration may include employees' amount of pay, pay methods, benefits, work hours, type of work performed, and qualifications required. It may also involve the workers' physical proximity and integration of tasks, the employer's supervisory or medical practice structure, and specific employee preferences. For example, union issues could involve the physical proximity of a group's work area to facilitate interaction among group members. If the work area was split across two floors of the same building, a union could see a negative effect on the group. The lack of proximity of the work spaces can create disintegration of work tasks and have a negative effect on the group's ability to perform its job, and therefore can be perceived as a burden on the workforce.

Union-Free Workforce

For a medical practice to maintain a union-free workplace, administrators must be experienced in knowing how to combat union organization efforts. The medical practice executive's human resource function, along with legal counsel, can help the medical group address local union activity, organizing tactics and targets, early warning signs of union involvement, lawful employer countermeasures, effective personnel policies and practices, and the employer's legal rights in dealing with a union.

The medical practice must provide its frontline supervisors and/or managers with the training necessary for lawful union avoidance. Managers must know what they can and cannot say about unions and unionization and how they must communicate effectively with the employees they oversee.

The practice executive should know how to effectively exercise the medical group's legal rights regarding assertive union campaigns, including how to lawfully communicate critical facts about collective bargaining, union dues, member obligations, strikes, and shutdowns to all employees. They must also know how to deal with union campaign handouts, postings, speeches, and videos that are lawful. Usually, the consideration of a union is caused by a lack of effective communication and problem solving with employees to address proper and effective employment practices.

Union Grievance Procedures

If a union has been established in a medical practice, the union contract will specify the grievance procedures. The process may be similar to that for nonunion employees, although it is best to read both policies for confirmation.

Competitive Wages

Unions will dictate a competitive wage package and a schedule for wage increases. Commonly, the program does not provide merit increases, but rather a fixed increase for each union employee.

Communication Plan

When the union and the medical practice sign a contract, there is a communication plan to ensure that the union employees understand the agreement on the practice's procedures and policies.

Employee Turnover

Employee turnover is a fact of life for all medical practices. A prepared executive should understand the reasons for employee turnover and the role it plays in creating an effective staff.

Voluntary Termination

Voluntary termination or resignation is when employees resign of their own free will. This type of termination is the most common. Management should try to determine as precisely as possible the reason for an employee's decision to leave. Typical reasons include securing a better position elsewhere, moving out of town, or experiencing personal dissatisfaction. In the last case, it is critical to find out the nature of the discontent. Turnover in a medical practice is costly. When the practice loses competent employees, it must spend considerable time and money to replace them and train new employees.

The best method for obtaining this information is through an exit interview. The interview can be summarized and this information sent to management for review. Obtaining information concerning voluntary termination can protect the practice from complaints by concerned federal, state, or local government agencies, and it can identify internal problems that are causing employee dissatisfaction.

Retirement

Traditionally, retirement has been at the end of a person's career. Today, however, retirement is seen more as a transition to a new stage of life. Prior to 1979, many organizations had retirement polices that made retirement mandatory at age 65.[11] The Age Discrimination in Employment Act of 1967 (ADEA), as amended, generally prohibits mandatory retirement at a certain age. However, practices can use age 65 as the usual retirement age when employees become eligible to retire. The difference is that no employee may be forced to retire at any age.

Some employers offer early retirement packages to encourage employees to retire earlier than they would otherwise. The *buyout* concept is an offer of cash inducements for early retirement. This approach allows employers to downsize in a way that does not discriminate. Compliance with all employment laws, including those covering employee benefits, is critical when a practice offers an early retirement package option.

Some employees prefer to go into semiretirement. Under this approach, a person reduces his or her normal working schedule to a predetermined lower number of hours per week. These can be configured as a reduced number of days per week or hours per day.

Another option is full retirement, but with the retired employee continuing to work for the employer as an independent contractor. This arrangement can be beneficial to both the employer and the employee as long as the individual is truly an independent contractor. There are significant risks with misclassifying employees as independent contractors, so you should consult with an attorney before proceeding with such an arrangement.

Retirement benefits vary greatly from one practice to another and are regulated by various federal and state laws including the Employee Retirement Income Security Act of 1974 (ERISA). The practice should work with its attorneys and financial professionals to determine which retirement benefits to offer employees. However, when a long-time employee does retire, many employers will recognize their contribution to the practice by hosting a retirement party and presenting them with a valuable gift or token of appreciation.

Layoffs

A layoff is a separation from employment, usually because of financial reasons, such as a decline in workload, a lower demand for service, a shortage of operating capital, or other factors over which the employee has no control. Layoffs are frequently referred to as *reductions in force* (RIFs).

Reductions in the workforce through layoffs are a fairly standard practice in some industries, especially as economic conditions change. In today's healthcare industry, organizations including medical practices are restructuring or merging together. Mergers often create situations where two people do the same job, one is selected to keep the position while the other person is either transferred to a new position or laid off.

The most important element in managing a layoff is developing a contingency plan for processing it. Procedures for identifying candidates for layoff should be established in advance.

Employers should use objective criteria to determine who is laid off. In the past, some organizations used longevity to determine who would be laid off. Today, most employers consider factors such as skills, ability, performance, and work history. Factors related to job performance give practice management more flexibility in retaining the best employees. However, layoff decisions based on performance are more difficult to defend, especially if the practice's performance evaluation tools are subjective or if performance history is poorly documented.

Layoff decisions must not involve unlawful discrimination. In addition, organizations employing more than 100 workers may fall under the Worker Adjustment and Retraining Notification Act of 1988, which requires advanced notification of certain types of layoffs, including mass layoffs and plant closings. Practices should consult with counsel to ensure compliance with all applicable federal and state laws when considering a layoff.

Depending on the type of employee benefits provided, the practice must decide which benefits, if any, will continue after a layoff. This issue is especially important in connection with group life, sickness, and accident insurance plans. Some medical practices continue these group insurance plans in force for a limited period of time, for example, 30 days, and/or make the conversions with the cost paid by the laid-off employee. Under the Consolidated Omnibus Budget Reconciliation Act of 1985 (COBRA), if an employee is terminated or loses benefits because of a reduction of hours, employers must extend employee health insurance coverage for up to 18 months with the coverage paid for by the employee.

The Consequences of Staff Reductions

Staff reductions through layoffs have serious effects not only on the laid-off employees but also on other employees. They create stress, and financial and emotional hardship to the laid-off employees and their families. Layoffs tend to decimate employee morale and loyalty to the organization. Consequently, the decision to lay off staff should be a last resort. It is extremely important that affected employees understand why they are being terminated.

When a medical practice concludes that a reduction in staff is needed, it usually comes on the heels of a significant business event. Dramatic fluctuations in patient census, new medical reimbursement methods or rates, mergers with other organizations, discontinuation of selected services, and other factors can create an adverse effect on profitability.

Many organizations choose to offer laid-off employees a severance package, although there is no mandatory government requirement to do so. Severance packages are a specific amount of money, months of pay, extended benefits, and/or outplacement benefits.

Practices who take this approach should consult with legal counsel to consider obtaining a release of claims in exchange for the severance benefits provided. A written statement of the terms of a severance package should be prepared before the termination meetings and given to employees during this meeting.

Most severance packages guarantee a specific lump sum of money or a set number of months of continued salary. They may also extend some benefits, such as health insurance, until the employee finds new employment or for a set number of months, whichever comes first. The packages typically range from two weeks' pay to several months depending on the employee's years of service. Some packages include outplacement services for laid-off employees to assist in obtaining other employment.

Termination Traps to Avoid

Despite adequate preparation, situations may arise that result in the terminating manager becoming flustered or deviating from the planned agenda during the termination meeting. Traps to avoid during termination meetings include:

- Turning the meeting into a performance evaluation;
- Trying to persuade the employee that the action is justified or getting into a discussion about details related to the termination decision;
- Discussing the supervisor's needs, feelings, or problems;
- Discussing alternatives to termination and allowing any bargaining;
- Bringing up past personality clashes, arguments, or situations;
- Reacting, whether agreeing or disagreeing, when the employee criticizes the employer;

- Arguing about anything;
- Shouting or raising the voice even if employee does so;
- Saying, "I know how you feel";
- Using a "this is a blessing in disguise" theme during the discussion;
- Saying, "I do not want to do this but..."; and
- Discussing the personal relationship with the employee.

Post-Termination Guidelines

A meeting with remaining staff, if appropriate, should be held immediately after a termination meeting, especially in the event of a RIF involving more than one employee. Often if just one employee is terminated involuntarily, it is appropriate to inform other employees that the terminated employee is no longer with the practice.

Remaining employees often bear the brunt of a staff reduction, whether it is through discharge, resignation, or layoffs. Although immediately relieved that they still have their jobs, employees often express feelings of concern, anger, guilt, sadness, and distrust. They are uncertain about their future. A meeting with remaining employees after a RIF should focus on alleviating fears, clearing up misunderstandings, opening communication about reassignment, if any, of the terminated employees' duties, and opening discussions about any concerns employees have. The meeting should convey how the practice will continue to move forward.

Outplacement services can be offered to employees whose jobs have been terminated to assist them with finding new employment. Outplacement involves the use of career-planning professionals, paid for by the former employer, to help terminated employees:

- Reassess their skill sets;
- Explore new job opportunities;
- Identify specific job leads;
- Acquire new job skills;
- Prepare appropriate materials, such as a résumé and cover letter;
- Sharpen interviewing skills; and
- Implement a strategic plan of action for their job search.

Because of the sensitive nature of outplacement, most employers outsource these services. The time needed to counsel and assist individuals in their job search can be extensive. Outplacement counseling can ease the pain of job loss and enable terminated employees to quickly find new employment.

Separation Agreements

Whenever an employer involuntarily terminates an employee, there is a risk of the employee filing a charge of discrimination with the Equal Employment Opportunity Commission (EEOC) or the equivalent agency or a lawsuit. One strategy to prevent expensive and time-consuming legal action is to offer the employee a separation agreement that includes a release of claims. By signing it, employees agree to release their claims in exchange for receiving additional pay or benefits to which they would not otherwise already be entitled to if they did not sign the separation agreement and release. Smaller practices often do not use separation agreements, but they can be helpful.

A separation agreement may delay an employee's termination, pending negotiation and implementing the terms of the agreement. Additional costs may be associated with using separation agreements, including extra monetary benefits given to the employee and the legal fees for drafting and negotiating such an agreement. A well-drafted, properly executed separation agreement effectively preempts a potential lawsuit. It provides finality to the termination because it prevents the employee from filing a lawsuit years down the road. However, separation agreements may not be feasible for all situations or employees. The employer cannot force the employee to sign the agreement even after expensive and time-consuming negotiations.

A separation agreement is not valid unless both sides are aware that they are getting something in exchange for something else. Employees should be fully informed and agree that they are not otherwise entitled to the additional consideration, such as severance pay, that they are receiving in exchange for the release of claims. The practice should also advise employees to consult with an attorney prior to signing the agreement.

Your medical practice should develop a procedure for preparing and negotiating separation agreements, for persuading terminated employees to execute separation agreements, and for ensuring that such agreements are legally binding. The Older Workers Benefit Protection Act of 1990 also requires certain additional provisions, including, but not limited to, specific periods of time to consider and revoke the agreement, which must be included to have a valid release of ADEA claims.

The practice should advise the employee of the seriousness of signing a separation agreement and provide him or her adequate time to discuss the matter with an attorney. Informing an employee of the ramifications of signing a separation agreement and allowing the employee reasonable time to consider the agreement and consult an attorney provides additional evidence that the employer did not coerce the employee into signing the agreement. Moreover, every factor illustrating that an employee signed the agreement voluntarily and knowingly supports its legality, including the fact that the agreement is written in basic language that an employee can understand, and shows that there was no coercion on the part of the employer. Further, an employee who was given the option of taking the agreement home, consulting with an attorney, and deciding whether to sign the agreement serves as persuasive evidence that the agreement was signed voluntarily, and without coercion, threats, or duress. This is particularly significant when an employee is not sophisticated or well educated.

Employee Records

Employee records are a primary source of data for managing, evaluating, and documenting human resource and employment-related activities. Employee records contain facts for myriad applications, including required reports to government agencies, reports for employees, reports on the effectiveness of human resource activities, and controls on operating expenses. Records can also highlight problem situations and provide data on salaries and wages. The type of employee information collected and maintained by management depends on its need for specific information, the size of the practice, and applicable laws.

Most organizations are subject to federal and state reporting regulations. Many of these regulations are employment related, but health, safety, and other types of regulations may also require reporting. Certain records are also kept to aid in employment decisions, such as hiring, promotions, training, discipline, layoffs, and terminations.

Medical practices should determine which records must be created and retained, and know how long to retain those records. Federal, state, or local laws may define how long certain documents must be retained. Employers should seek the advice of legal counsel on the requirements for retention of documents in relation to charges of discrimination, pending litigation, or potential litigation.

Human Resource Information System

A human resource information system (HRIS), sometimes called a *human resource management system*, is usually a hosted software solution that can help human resource professionals track and maintain many human resource functions, including employee records. Most HRIS solutions also offer features that allow employees to view and generate reports. Many small businesses, including medical practices, are finding that an HRIS is an inexpensive, yet highly valuable method to manage many human resource functions.

HRISs range from advanced, enterprise-wide systems to simple solutions with limited features. They range from *software-as-a-service* solutions to hosted solutions to in-house solutions. Prices range from inexpensive, encompassing only the basic human resource functions, to expensive enterprise solutions. There are many different HRISs available, and selecting one should be based on the needs of your medical practice. Your information technology (IT) department or IT advisor can help determine which solution is the best fit for the practice needs.

Typical HRIS functionality includes:

- Payroll;
- Employee attendance and leave;
- Performance evaluations;
- Benefits administration;
- Employee records;
- Recruiting, including applicant tracking;
- Training, rewards, and bonus histories;
- Reporting; and
- Health and safety records.

Employee Files

It is crucial for employers to carefully maintain employee files, knowing which documents to create, which documents to keep, where they should be kept, and how long to keep them. Most, but not all, employee records are kept in employee files, whether physical or electronic. Other policy issues that need to be addressed are destruction of files, employees' access to their files, and maintaining appropriate confidentiality.

Employee File Contents

Typically, most employee files include the following:

- Preemployment documents, including job application forms, résumés, results of preemployment reference checks, and results of any nonmedical preemployment tests;
- Forms acknowledging receipt of an employee handbook;
- Personal and emergency contact information;
- Employment history, including date of hire, initial salary, dates of raises, explanations for raises, job classifications, work locations, layoffs, and terminations;
- Attendance records;
- Education and training records;
- Performance evaluations;
- Recognition and awards;
- Coaching, warning, and disciplinary records;
- W-4 forms; and
- Documents related to employment termination.

Employee file maintenance policies and practices should be developed keeping in mind applicable federal and state laws related to record-keeping, employee privacy, retention and destruction of records, and accessibility of employee files.

Documents to Be Kept Separate from the Employee File

Certain types of employment records must be kept separately from employee files. A general rule is that any documentation that may not lawfully be considered when making personnel decisions should not be kept in the employee file. The EEOC recommends that any records of an employee's gender, race, ethnicity, or sexual orientation that may be required for reporting purposes be kept separately from the employee file.

Medical records must be kept separately from employee files. Examples of medical records include:

- Information about drug use other than illegal drug use;
- Workers' compensation claims and correspondence;
- Results for medical inquiries or examinations; and
- Claims submitted for medical, disability, or life insurance.

Records relating to benefits administration and insurance should also be kept separately because these may contain medical records. Self-identification forms from disabled employees, as well as requests for accommodation, should not be kept in employee files because such documents may also include medical records. Other documents that should not be kept in employee files include I-9 forms, any other documents regarding an employee's eligibility to work in the United States, and documents related to child support or wage garnishment.

Accessibility and Confidentiality

Because employee files contain private and confidential information, great effort should be made to maintain the privacy and confidentiality of these files. A growing number of medical practices are using an HRIS to store and manage employee files. If the practice uses electronic employee files, ensure that the hosted solution is secure, employees have secure and controlled access to their employee files, and only designated human resource professionals and supervisors have controlled access. If the practice chooses to use physical employee files, employees should have access to their own file at reasonable times and at reasonable intervals.

There is no federal law that requires private sector employers to provide employees access to their personnel files. However, some states have laws governing employees' access to their employee files. State laws differ but may explain rights and define procedures for employees who wish to inspect, copy, correct, or expunge information contained in their employee file. These laws may also contain exceptions and limitations to access.

Regardless of whether there is an applicable state law, medical practices should have a well-defined policy on how and when employees have access to their employee files. Such a policy should comply with applicable state law and take into account the employer's and employees' interests. If the practice has physical employee files, you must ensure that the confidentiality of other files is not compromised when allowing an employee access to his or her employee file. In addition, the practice must provide supervision of employees while they have access to their files to guarantee that the contents are not removed or altered without consent. Practices may consider limiting access to specific days and times and requiring advanced notice so that the employee's file can be pulled and reviewed to remove any confidential materials.

If your practice uses an HRIS solution to store and manage employee files, you must ensure that the employee cannot delete or alter documents or information in the file. That said, most systems do allow employees to update certain information within their employee files such as addresses, phone numbers, emergency contacts, and so forth.

Be cautious about giving out employee information. Medical practices should refuse to release employment information to third parties without the employee's written authorization. If employee files are released without the employee's consent, the employee could claim an invasion of privacy.

Record-Keeping, Reporting, and Government Requirements

State and federal laws require employers to create and maintain certain employment-related records. Below is a brief summary of some of the laws governing record-keeping. Medical practices should work with legal counsel to ensure they are complying with all applicable laws regarding record-keeping, which may include regulations not mentioned here.

Federal Insurance Contributions Act of 1935

Several laws and regulations require employers to keep records regarding employee compensation and mandatory federal income taxes. Federal law, including the Federal Insurance Contributions Act (FICA), the Federal Unemployment Tax Act of 1939, and federal income tax withholdings regulations, requires employers to keep employee records for four years. These records include, but are not limited to:

- Name;
- Address;
- Social Security number;
- Gender;
- Date of birth;
- Occupation;
- Job classification;
- Total compensation;
- Tax forms;
- Hours worked;
- Wages subject to tax withholdings;
- Actual taxes withheld from wages; and
- Payments to annuities, pension, accident, health, and other benefits.

Maintaining such records for four years may not be long enough in certain circumstances. Further, states may impose additional requirements.

Equal Pay Act of 1963

The EEOC requires employers covered by the Equal Pay Act (those covered by the Fair Labor Standards Act of 1938 [FLSA]) to keep certain records required by the Department of Labor. Covered employers must preserve records made in the regular course of business that relate to the payment of wages, wage rates, job evaluations, job descriptions, merit systems, seniority systems, and collective bargaining agreements. Covered employers must also keep records of any practice that explains the basis for payment of higher wages to employees of one sex than to employees of the other sex in the same establishment. These records may be important in determining whether a difference in wages is based on a factor other than gender. These records must be retained for at least two years.

Occupational Safety and Health Act

The Occupational Safety and Health Act of 1970 requires most employers to maintain records of occupational injuries, illnesses, and deaths. The records consist of a log and summary of occupational illnesses and injuries, a supplementary record of each occupational injury or illness, and an annual summary of information contained in the log, all of which must be retained for five years following the end of the calendar year that the records cover. The log and annual summary must be completed for each location that is expected to remain in operation for one year or longer. For example, a medical practice with two offices must keep a separate log and annual summary at each office. An Injury and Illness Incident Report must be completed for each work-related injury or illness that occurs.

Certain employers, including those with the potential for workplace exposure to blood-borne pathogens and other toxic substances, should prepare an *exposure control plan* to eliminate or minimize employee exposure or provide documentation that demonstrates compliance. These documents usually include detailed records of training, exposure monitoring, medical monitoring, and others. The Occupational Safety and Health Administration (OSHA) also requires an employer to preserve and maintain employee medical and exposure records for the term of the employee's employment plus 30 years. Workers' compensation laws in each state may also require similar reports.

Title VII of the Civil Rights Act of 1964

Under Title VII and corresponding EEOC regulations, an employer who maintains employment records (any records having to do with hiring, transfer, demotion, promotion, layoff, termination, rates of pay, and selection for training programs), must keep the records for a period of one year from the date the records were made or one year from the date of the personnel action, whichever is longer. In the case of an involuntary termination, personnel records should be kept for one year following the date of the termination. When a charge of discrimination has been filed, employers must preserve all records relevant to the charge until the final disposition of the charge.

Americans with Disabilities Act of 1990

The Americans with Disabilities Act (ADA) incorporates Title VII's provision requiring certain records to be kept. If an employer keeps employment or employee records, including requests for reasonable accommodation, the employer must preserve those records for a period of one year from the date the record is created or one year from the date of the personnel action involved, whichever is longer. If a discrimination charge is filed, the employer must keep all records relevant to the charge until the final disposition of the charge.

Under the ADA, an employer must maintain all medical records for applications and employees separately from employee files. In addition, the ADA requires confidential treatment of such medical files.

Fair Labor Standards Act of 1938

Under the FLSA, employers are required to make and keep records, generally including identifying information of employees and data about hours worked and wages earned. Records for nonexempt employees should generally include:

- Name, Social Security number, address and ZIP code;
- Sex;
- Date of birth, if younger than 19;
- Occupation;
- Time and day of the week on which the employee's workweek begins;
- Regular hourly rate of pay;
- Hours worked by the employee each workday;
- Total hours the employee worked each workweek;
- Total daily or weekly straight-time earnings;
- Basis on which wages are paid;
- Total overtime earnings for each workweek;
- Additions to or deductions from wages;
- Total wages per pay period; and
- Date of payment and pay period covered by the payment.

Payroll records, collective bargaining agreements, and sales and purchase records must be retained for at least three years. Records on which computations are based must be retained for at least two years.

Age Discrimination in Employment Act of 1967

Under the ADEA, a covered employer must keep records on each employee, which include name, date of birth, address, occupation, rate of pay, and weekly compensation. These records must be kept for at least three years.

The ADEA also requires employers to keep records of the following for one year after the date of the personnel action:

- Applications for employment, résumés, and any other form of employment inquiry in response to job advertisements, including records related to hiring decisions;
- Promotion, transfer, selections for training, demotion, layoff, recall, or discharge of any employee;
- Job orders submitted by the employer to an employment agency or labor organization for recruitment of employees for job openings;
- Test papers completed by applicants for any position that disclose the results of any employer-administered aptitude or other employment test considered by the employer in connection with any personnel action;
- Physical examination results considered in connection with any personnel action; and
- Any advertising related to job openings, promotions, training programs, or opportunities for overtime work.

Employers must also keep on file any employee benefit plan (such as pension and insurance plans) and any written seniority or merit system for the full period the plan or system is in effect and for at least one year after its termination.

Immigration Reform and Control Act of 1986

Employers are required to have all new employees complete the I-9 form to verify they are eligible to work in the United States. As mentioned earlier, these forms should be kept separately from the employee files in a designated file for the U.S. Citizenship and Immigration Services or electronically. The forms must be completed within three business days after the first day of employment for pay and made available for inspection by the Department of Labor or the Department of Homeland Security. Employers must keep I-9 forms for either three years or one year after termination, whichever is longer. Some states also have laws related to verification of work eligibility that may contain additional record-keeping requirements.

Employee Retirement Income Security Act of 1974

Under ERISA, covered retirement plans are subject to many reporting and disclosure requirements. Government agencies that require reporting under ERISA are the Department of Labor, the Pension Benefit Guaranty Corporation, and the Internal Revenue Service. ERISA usually requires plan administrators to:

- Submit an annual return and report of employee benefit plan;
- Provide plan participants a summary plan description on enrollment, when any changes are made to the plan, or every 10 years;
- Provide information about the plan on written request of a plan participant or beneficiary;
- Submit the summary plan description to the Department of Labor on request; and
- Provide statements to employees who leave the organization and are eligible for benefits.

Check with your financial advisor and your accountant to determine your medical practice's specific reporting requirements.

Employee Polygraph Protection Act of 1988

The Employee Polygraph Protection Act generally prevents most private employers from using lie detector tests. In the rare event a polygraph test is permitted, the employer must provide certain notices to the examiner and the examinee. Employers requesting a polygraph test must retain records for a minimum of three years from the date of the polygraph test or from the date the test is requested if no test is conducted.

Labor Relations and Union Reporting

Under the Labor-Management Reporting and Disclosure Act of 1959, private employers must report certain financial transactions to the Department of Labor. For example, employers must report certain expenditures or arrangements that are made for the purpose of interfering with, restraining, or coercing employees in the exercise of their bargaining or representation rights. In addition, employers who engage a consultant to influence employees not to join a labor union must submit a record of the consultant's fee and expenses.

Unemployment Laws

To administer unemployment compensation programs, each state's Employment Security Commission requests quarterly reports of turnover from employers. This information is compiled regionally and nationally by the Department of Labor's Bureau of Labor Statistics to provide valuable research data to companies.

Legal Hold Obligations

When a medical practice reasonably anticipates litigation, it must ensure that it retains all documents (including electronic documents) relevant to that potential litigation, otherwise it risks the imposition of sanctions for spoliation of evidence. This also applies in the context of threatened litigation or government investigations, audits, or proceedings.

To prevent the accidental destruction of relevant information and documents, a medical practice must suspend its routine document destruction policies and issue a *legal hold* to all individuals who may have relevant documents in order to ensure the preservation of relevant documents and electronically stored information. The legal hold should require the retention of all relevant documents until the conclusion of the litigation, investigation, audit, or proceeding. Medical practices should consult legal counsel to develop a legal hold policy and to comply with its legal hold obligations in the event of potential litigation or a government investigation, audit, or proceeding.

Conclusion

There is more to employee retention than annual performance evaluations. Key skills required to keep and motivate your employees include knowledge of labor relations and employment record-keeping as well as the ability to motivate, resolve conflict, build teams, and provide career development opportunities for both clinical and nonclinical staff.

Notes

1. *State of the American Workforce,* Gallup, Jan. 1, 2014, www.gallup.com/services/178514/state-american-workplace.aspx.
2. Marshall M. Baker and Kenneth M. Hekman, *Physician Policies: A Practical Guide to Governance Issues* (Englewood, CO: Medical Group Management Association, 2011), xviii.
3. Marshall and Hekman, *Physician Policies,* 225.
4. Rade Vukmir, *Physician Contracting Guidebook* (Englewood, CO: Medical Group Management Association and American Medical Association, 2014), 3.
5. Reprinted by permission of the publisher, from *Generations at Work* by Ron Zemke, Claire Raines, and Bob Filipczak ©2013 Susan Zemke, Claire Raines, and Bob Filipczak, AMACOM books, division American Management Association International, New York, NY. All rights reserved. www.amacombooks.org.
6. Rudi Plettnix, *Emerging Leader: Implications for Engagement and Retention* (Brussels, Belgium: Center for Creative Leadership, 2006).
7. Adrienne Hill and Rose Wagner, "Growing Pains: Onboarding New Physicians," *MGMA Connexion* 13, no. 2 (2013): 35–36.
8. Claire Raines, *Connecting Generations: The Sourcebook for a New Workplace* (Menlo Park, CA: Crisp Publications, 2003), 44.
9. "The Average Employee Lawsuit Costs $250,000...How Safe Is Your Company?" CERS: Cutting Edge Recruiting Solutions, Sept. 11, 2012, www.cersnow.com/blog/the-average-employee-lawsuit-costs-250000how-safe-is-your-company/.
10. Courtney Price and Alys Novak, *HR Policies & Procedures Manual for Medical Practices,* 5th ed. (Englewood, CO: Medical Group Management Association, 2015), 237.
11. "Amendment of the Age Discrimination in Employment Act of 1967," *Illinois Municipal Review,* Illinois Periodicals Online (IPO), Northern Illinois University Libraries, December 1986, www.lib.niu.edu/1986/im861220.html.

Chapter 3

Training and Developing Staff and Understanding Employment Law

Staff Training and Development

Every medical practice, if it wants to gain market share and become or remain successful, must provide its employees with ongoing training and professional development. Whether it is pursued through internal means (staff meetings, training sessions, etc.) or through external methods (association meetings, consultants, paid training sessions), continuing education builds a solid foundation of knowledge for employees to better perform their jobs. Every medical group needs its employees to have continuing-education updates on safety (e.g., Occupational Safety and Health Administration [OSHA], universal precautions, fire prevention) and compliance (e.g., the Health Insurance Portability and Accountability Act of 1996 [HIPAA], correct billing practices), along with updates on technology and regulatory changes (e.g., Medicare, Medicaid, state laws). Continuing education may also be needed to keep an employee licensed or registered in a particular profession and to improve interpersonal, leadership, or other personal skill sets.

The medical practice needs to determine, in advance, what it will pay for training the employee. Employee training can be very costly but is usually worth the investment. In fact, costs are often higher if the practice doesn't invest in its employees because of lost productivity, mistakes, citations, violation fees, fines, and other risk management issues.

Effective training requires a positive learning environment, quality materials, motivated and incentivized employees, and adult learning models based on the needs of the group being trained. Training sessions must be staffed by trained professionals as opposed to experts in content material, and by people who can teach adults using a variety of teaching methods.

The key competencies necessary to effectively manage the training and development of staff include:

- Fostering a culture and providing an environment of learning and professional development;
- Overseeing training, including orientation, technical skills, career development, compliance, and cross-training;
- Establishing policies and procedures for training;
- Maintaining an updated employee handbook and updated policies and procedures; and
- Complying with employment laws.

Training and Development Philosophy

Medical groups need to be aware of the ongoing changes facing the practice of medicine. To keep up with the changes in reimbursement, coding, managed care, compliance, and clinical practice, the employer must provide the employee with appropriate formats for learning. With the proliferation of technological advances, the medical practice executive should look at new options to improve results and outcomes. The medical group and its employees are becoming more sophisticated consumers and are demanding better access to information. Employees want and seek more professional development opportunities, better access to those resources, and greater flexibility to learn.

Measuring Training Value to the Organization

The value to the organization of training can be measured through integration with appropriate evaluation tools. Evaluation tools are quick and objective ways to identify the strengths and weaknesses of the learning. Evaluation is drawn from the employee evaluation, participant learning, achievement of the behavior change sought, and the overall effect on the organization. Accomplishment of these areas provides the demonstrated value of training and shows how it can affect the medical group's revenue and profit, employee satisfaction, market share, and patient satisfaction.

Present Cost vs. Future Investment

Training is a budgeted line item, and its impact is measurable by future outcomes. For example, a medical assistant who performs charge entry must be familiar with Current Procedural Terminology (CPT®)* and the International Classification of Diseases, 9th revision (ICD-9) and ICD-10 codes and needs to have knowledge of appropriate documentation for billing. Effective training will help the employee to question mistakes and capture possible lost charges or incorrectly coded charge tickets. Medical billers may be able to handle billing error follow-up better if they are trained on the correct coding edits and how to communicate with front-end staff about how to avoid these kinds of errors. This training leads to faster payment and fewer errors to track. The cost to handle errors is reduced, so the staff can focus more energy on doing things correctly than on fixing mistakes. Failure to provide training up front will result in poorer performance and outcomes in the future.

The medical practice executive should plan for employee training and determine who is eligible, how training needs are determined, and how those services are obtained. Reimbursement may be prepaid or paid after successful completion of the program. Tuition coverage may be a separate benefit to provide employee training or may be used to let an employee pursue higher education in a field that would benefit the medical group, such as business, nursing, or allied health.

Training and Development Policies

Training and development policies communicate to employees the importance the medical group places on employee training, education, development, and job enrichment, along with optimizing productivity and profit. Such a policy must ensure that opportunities are available to all staff members.

A training and development policy should cover when and how to announce these opportunities, eligibility for attendance, required approvals, and types of programs endorsed by the medical group. At the very least, the group should offer training and development programs that increase existing employee knowledge and skills. A training and development policy should stress the importance of having supervisors encourage their staff to attend training programs and to groom competent employees for promotional opportunities. Building a pipeline of well-trained employees ready for the next step ensures productive succession.

Change Management through Continuing Education

Medical practice executives not only need to implement specific solutions to changes, but, equally important, they need to establish context for change. Often, staff and partners are so absorbed in their own functions that they are not aware of larger trends in the healthcare or business environment. The medical group executive must continue to monitor trends and stay up to date in order to establish context when asking staff or partners to make changes. Knowing there is a Medicare prescription drug benefit, and knowing both how the benefit works and how it is paid for, for example, can help the executive communicate with partners and staff regarding prescribing patterns. Similarly, understanding the Internal Revenue Service intermediate sanctions rules can help an executive in the nonprofit sector clarify why additional documentation and scrutiny of business-related expenses are necessary. Understanding the status of class-action lawsuits against hospitals regarding billing practices for the uninsured helps the executive explain why inquiries are being made regarding the group's practices around billing the uninsured.

Executives can keep up with information and change in many ways. The primary methods involve memberships and continuing education. Memberships in state or national groups such as the Medical Group Management Association (MGMA®), Healthcare Financial Management Association, or local medical societies can provide material such as monthly journals and electronic discussion groups, many of which are tailored to specific needs. Every specialty publishes a variety of journals that offer articles and advice regarding medical group management issues.

A plethora of non-specialty-specific journals are also aimed at assisting the medical practice with its business on issues ranging from coding alerts to medical economics. In many cases, monitoring the general press, business press, and online news outlets can give an executive tips on upcoming knowledge needs, issues, and trends.

Most professional organizations also sponsor numerous continuing-education events where executives can attend various workshops and lectures on subjects they need to learn. These events also offer opportunities to meet with others facing the same or similar challenges and to learn from colleagues how to approach specific issues. In fact, MGMA even requires its members to document 50 hours of continuing education over a three-year period to maintain certification. Members can also show their commitment to continuing education and professional growth by obtaining Certified Medical Practice Executive (CMPE) status.

Scheduling for Training

Freeing up staff to be trained is a logistical challenge. Time must be budgeted to allow staff to be appropriately oriented and trained. Let us look at some methods of creative scheduling and flexible staffing that are needed to accommodate and allow all staff members to be trained.

Replacement schedules. Depending on the size of the medical group, employees may be specifically hired to cover schedules of other staff members when they are being trained. Replacement schedules allow staff members to focus on the training at hand with the knowledge and comfort that their shifts are being appropriately covered.

Release time. A medical group needs to determine under what circumstances an employee will be allowed company time or paid release time to attend an educational program.

Overtime considerations. Although the goal is to use part-time and as-needed staff to cover employee training, there may be times when certain staff members will need to work overtime to accommodate the training needs of the organization. Overtime may need to be used for large-scale training projects, such as computer conversions, implementation of an electronic health record (EHR) system, or installation of new equipment.

Paid Attendance, Meeting Time, and Continuing Medical Education Policy

Paid attendance may be specifically defined and there may be a cap on dollars or days available for training. For example, a physician may be given one week of continuing medical education days paid by the medical group not to exceed $3,000 per calendar year. This guideline helps every employee to manage expenses and time away from the practice appropriately.

Training Goals

To provide high-quality patient care in a cost-efficient manner, healthcare organizations must create a work environment that develops competent employees. Because the quality of patient care is directly related to the knowledge, skills, abilities, and attitudes of the medical practice's staff, employee training and development programs should aim to improve performance and advance employee qualifications. Specific goals of training and development programs may include:

- Improving the knowledge, skills, and ability of employees;
- Transferring the acquired skills and accumulated knowledge of experienced staff to less experienced employees; and
- Training staff to accomplish current and future organizational requirements.

The specific training and development objectives and efforts of practices vary significantly, depending on management philosophy and group size. Regardless of size, management should plan and arrange for appropriate training and development opportunities for all employees.

Types of Training

Training content determination is a multidisciplinary group process. Usually groups identify more topics and issues than what can possibly be covered. Teams can help prioritize topics and level of detail needed for training, and this, in turn, largely determines the type of training that is pursued.

Orientation and onboarding. All employees receive a general orientation to the organization. This usually includes an overview of the medical group, training in the group's practices and policies, and a departmental orientation. These orientations can take hours or weeks to complete, depending on the complexity and level of detail needed for the employee.

Supervisors and managers. A management development program that creates a guide and/or template for the new manager to follow allows the manager to be aware of those areas that he or she needs to know within the organization prior to completing a full orientation.

Technical and skilled duties. Depending on the nature of the job, an employer may train the staff on technical and skill-based employment functions. Or they may expect a core level of technical and skill-based knowledge but train the employee specifically on the organizational-based skill needed for the job.

Career development. An employer may support an employee through career development opportunities. The employee may be afforded the opportunity to seek additional training and career advancement at the employer's expense. The long-term expectations of the employee must be clearly stated prior to the employee seeking these educational opportunities.

Certification. Certification allows the employee to demonstrate a core competency or knowledge in a specific field of study. Certification provides acknowledgment of skill, knowledge, education, and proficiency achieved in an area. Sometimes certification is required for initial employment or to continue being employed in the medical group. Board certification for medical practice administrators (i.e., CMPE) can be earned through MGMA.

Cross-training. Cross-training a staff member allows the staff to be flexible in staffing schedules and allows staff to take time off without the worry of how the employee's tasks will be performed during the employee's absence. It also allows multiple people to be involved in a task and to provide creative suggestions and ideas about how to improve a system or process.

If cross-training is not done well, a person may assume a task and perform the task poorly through learned bad habits or behaviors. Cross-training must be continuously evaluated to ensure that employees provide quality in the work performed.

Adult Learning Styles

Employee training programs can be developed and implemented by the medical practice or can be outsourced to other agencies, schools, or organizations that focus on specific topics or issues. Training programs can take many forms to help the adult learner. An adult learner generally approaches learning differently than a young student does. Adults are usually more self-guided in learning, bring added experience to the learning process, expect more from the learning experience, and will challenge any learning that doesn't make sense.

Learning by doing. Many people learn best by doing. A medical assistant can learn all about how and why and under what circumstances to draw blood and about the tools needed to perform the function, but there is nothing like practicing on oneself and others to become skilled. Learning by doing can be invaluable as long as there is a written plan to demonstrate proficiency and competency in a learned function.

Didactic teaching. Common classroom settings, which nearly every American has experienced at some time through formal education, provide a lesson plan, reading time, class interaction, possible homework, and a test to measure whether the adult learner has mastered the skill or body of knowledge.

Mentoring and coaching. Mentoring is a method of supporting a new employee to learn new tasks and duties from an exceptionally performing employee. Sometimes mentoring supports a current employee who is interested in learning new job tasks or functions.

Mentoring must be carefully planned because some employees are exceptional employees but poor mentors or trainers. Some people know how to perform a job well but do not know how to show someone else how to do the same job. A mentor should be an active listener who is patient, willing to explain things repetitively, and able to break down job tasks into smaller segments and describe how they fit together. Many times, a mentor can become the company trainer or coach.

Coaching provides individual one-on-one attention to an employee needing greater supervision and encouragement. Coaching is a cyclical process that works with the adult learner and determines what kind of support the employee needs depending on the personal traits of the employee. The coaching support will depend on what part of the cycle the employee is in with respect to the task being mastered and learned. Usually, the new employee is a beginner and is enthusiastic to learn a new skill, but may be apprehensive about making mistakes. The learner needs clear instructions, constant feedback, emotional support, and praise when a task is learned well.

The next level of coaching is providing extensive technical and emotional support for the employee so he or she is not discouraged from performing a task because of mistakes made. Also, poor techniques should not become learned, as bad habits can be difficult to break.

Once the employee has learned the new skill, the coach provides guidance to reinforce the skill learned until the employee has mastered the skill and has become an expert. At that point, the employee needs little direction or support. The employee embraces the new task, takes ownership of it, and begins to take on extra tasks and responsibilities. The coach can then begin to work with the employee on new skills.

Coaching helps to build employee confidence and affirms that the employee is performing aspects of the job correctly. Coaching also provides positive reinforcement of a job well done.

Self-directed learning. With the proliferation of computer technology, numerous self-directed learning modules can support an employee in learning to perform new tasks and functions independently. These programs comprise reading, example problems, case studies, and questions to answer prior to taking a test. A self-directed program can be very effective for a well-motivated, organized adult. If the adult struggles with self-motivation, organizing and/or prioritizing workload, and/or using computers or reading booklets, a self-directed program may not work well.

Group interaction. Providing a forum for group interaction can be a powerful and effective way for an employee to learn. Group interaction can promote personal growth, teach professional skills, and provide a cost-effective method to learn tasks and skills. The learning can be customized based on the particular group brought together. The group interaction can be based on small work groups, large forums, workshops, or even online Web-based computer classes with dialogue forums.

Training Formats

Training can be delivered to students in a variety of ways. Formats can range from computer media to books.

Computer media. Computer-based training allows the employee to use specific software on a self-directed basis to learn a new skill. The employee must have a basic level of comfort with computers to perform these tasks. Videos are popular for training purposes, and now interactive videos in DVD or online streaming formats are available on Internet and intranet sites. The low cost for this technology relative to staff travel and per diem costs has made it a convenient medium for training.

Interactive training. Interactive training allows the employee to participate in the process and learn by doing. A phlebotomy training class that allows the employee to practice drawing blood is more effective than just reading a book. Interactive training may involve a skills lab where employees can work in a simulated setting (e.g., in a patient exam room or on a telephone for customer service skills).

Role playing. Role-playing exercises allow the employee to test practical knowledge learned in a real-life situation, but in a manner that is safe and protected. For example, a manager may learn how to have a critical conversation with an employee about poor work performance. A role-playing session lets the manager talk with a trainer who pretends to be the disgruntled employee. The two can try out different situations to let the manager see whether the learned skills can be practically applied in a situation. The trainer provides feedback and constructive input on areas that can be improved in this situation.

Lecturer. A lecture or speaker presentation is another common educational format that is popular with large groups of people. The speaker may use electronic slide presentations or paper handouts to cover the material and allow questions either during the presentation or at the end.

Group discussion. A group discussion allows people to ask questions and hear different perspectives about an issue or topic. The group discussion may be focused on a series of questions that are asked of the group after the presentation of materials. Getting the group involved helps to affirm the topic and reinforce the knowledge.

Books. Books, workbooks, resource manuals, training manuals, and other printed material have been the most traditional resources for training. However, with the development of the Internet and Web-based applications, more books are being placed online.

Online education. Educational resources are now available online. A participant can log on to any computer with Internet access and take a class. The technology monitors modules completed, tests taken, and completion of the training program. These applications make training much more accessible, convenient, and flexible. Many applications provide the participant with videos to watch and even present opportunities to submit information and written materials for the reviewer to evaluate.

Outsourced Training

The use of outsourcing vs. an in-house training staff depends on the needs of the organization. Usually, the larger the organization, the more likely the medical group will pursue an in-house training staff. Smaller medical groups do not have the ability to hire someone full time to handle in-house needs.

An outsourced training program can be efficient, cost-effective, and provide a strong service level for the customer because the client provides these services routinely to a large group of employees. Outsourcing allows the medical practice to focus its energy on other aspects of the operation. Every medical group has a limited number of human resource staff members whose services are focused on serving the employees and improving service excellence. With outsourced training, a physician group can use the best practices, systems, and educational venues with a smaller investment than creating, maintaining, and improving an in-house training program.

For certain areas, however, as a medical group expands and grows, there is value in having in-house staff. A medical practice executive may bring certain training functions in house (e.g., computer training, compliance, and safety training) but continue to outsource other training functions (e.g., cardiopulmonary resuscitation or CPT training). Regardless of the decision made, a medical group practice must evaluate and discern how in-house and outsourced training will be used to educate employees.

Training the Trainer

Training the trainer allows a medical group to have one person or a group of people trained on a specific application or area of training and then bring that information back to the organization for on-site training and implementation. It can be project specific (e.g., EHR implementation), department specific (e.g., nursing orientation), or organization specific (e.g., information technology, computer, and clinical training). The trainer needs to be comfortable with using adult learning principles and focus on a program that develops objectives, selects the appropriate training method, develops training aids, and uses facilitation and problem-solving skills. A mechanism should also be in place to evaluate the training sessions.

Employee Orientation and Onboarding

The goal of employee orientation and onboarding is to reduce turnover and increase retention. Effective orientation programs help newly hired employees learn not only about their individual job duties, benefits, and policies, but also which behaviors the practice values and how their jobs contribute to the overall success of the medical group. Your employees should understand that each of them is vitally important to effective and high-quality patient care.

Some medical practices orient new employees by spending a few minutes giving a tour of the facility, introducing coworkers, showing them their workspace, and then having someone show them how to do their job tasks. This type of orientation program fails to cover many critical elements that help and encourage new employees to perform at their best. Others offer half-day, one-day, or two-day new employee orientation programs that provide a more thorough overview of the medical group.

Onboarding

Onboarding is a growing human resource trend advocating a comprehensive approach to bringing on new hires that goes beyond traditional orientation programs. Onboarding is the process of bringing new employees into the organization by providing information, training, mentoring, and coaching during their first 6 to 12 months of employment. It helps new employees more quickly contribute to the organization, increase their comfort level, reinforce their decision to join the organization, and enhance productivity, and it encourages employee commitment, engagement, and retention. Research has also demonstrated that, more than traditional orientation programs, onboarding reduces stress and the chance of employees quitting soon after starting.

Onboarding and new employee orientation programs help employees develop a self-identity and a team spirit, which contribute to healthy attitudes toward the medical group and can lower absenteeism and employee turnover. They are an effective way to communicate not only that the medical practice demands full effort from its employees to maximize productivity and the quality of services, but also that the practice values and respects its employees. These programs also inform new hires about the practice's policy prohibiting unlawful discrimination and harassment.

Keep in mind that your medical group's Website gives the first impression of your office, followed by the interview process and the type of new employee orientation program you offer. As mentioned earlier, all of these influence newly hired employees' long-term commitment to the practice.

To reinforce the medical group's commitment to its employees, the human resource department or administrator should consistently follow up with each new employee during the first few months of employment to see if there is a need for more information and/or training. Onboarding programs that include mentoring and coaching are more comprehensive and help to ensure a successful transition into the medical practice.

New Employee Orientation Design

At a minimum, the practice's orientation program should consist of two distinct parts: a general organizational overview and a departmental orientation. The organizational overview should provide information on the group's history, mission, values, policies, and compensation and benefits. The general overview should also introduce the practice's strategic plan and structure. This training should be delivered by the human resource department or person responsible for these activities.

The frequency of the orientation program depends on the size of the medical group, employee turnover, and the number of new employees. In a small medical practice, employee orientation may be conducted on an individual basis as new employees are hired, and usually, the person responsible for employee administration conducts the orientation. Medium-sized practices might offer this program once every few months, while larger practices may hold these programs more often. Ideally, orientation should be scheduled during the first week of work.

The second part of the orientation concerns information about essential functions and standards of performance. Generally the immediate supervisor facilitates this departmental orientation to introduce new employees to their job duties and responsibilities and their department's goals, performance standards, and policies. This orientation also familiarizes employees with the work area, coworkers, and work rules.

The supervisor should follow up the orientation with effective, consistent communication with the employee, include making the employee feel welcomed and relaxed by greeting him or her each morning and by encouraging questions. An assigned mentor can help facilitate this process.

The Link between Physician Retention and Orientation

When developing and implementing a formal physician orientation program, link the objectives of physician retention and orientation. An orientation program permits newly hired physicians to meet senior management and learn about the practice's strategies, market, managed care relationships, clinical programs, residency teaching, rotations, continuing education, research opportunities, risk management, and recruiting.

Linking your physician orientation and retention programs begins with the components listed in Exhibit 3.1.

When the employment market was more fluid, medical groups regarded retention-related orientation programs as an afterthought of the recruitment function. This often limited physician orientation to a rote explanation of the rules, compensation, and other company policies necessary to ensure smooth personnel functions. Now the emphasis in orientation is moving from the end of the recruitment function to the beginning of the retention process.

Onboarding Design

Onboarding is intended to be a multifaceted and customized approach and typically lasts from 6 to 12 months. It goes beyond the typical half-day to two-day new employee orientation program by facilitating social relations with the supervisor, managers, and coworkers.

Most onboarding programs are designed to get feedback from new hires at the end of the first week, first month, first three months, and so on, asking different questions at each stage to learn how engaged or connected the new hire feels to the medical practice. Typical questions begin with asking about the recruiting process and how the first few days met the employee's expectations. Later feedback inquires about any issues he or she might be struggling with, whether the employee has the necessary tools to complete his or her job, and then shifts focus to the employee's strategic goals.

EXHIBIT 3.1

Linking Physician Orientation and Retention Programs[1]

Establish board policy	Put the elements of this plan, including goals and objectives, into writing and get approval at the board level.
Designate responsibility	Specific individuals should monitor, manage, and be held responsible for retention duties; larger practices should consider establishing a retention committee.
Recruit wisely	Many issues that lead physicians to leave a practice can be discovered through careful screening, assessment, and interviewing of potential recruits.
Conduct thorough orientation	Plan to show newcomers the community, including hospitals, clinic sites, and nursing homes with which the practice interacts.
Introduce newcomers	Introduce newcomers to other physicians in the community, including those they will deal with for referrals or consultations, and certain other key players from outside the practice, such as administrators of referring facilities.
Develop a marketing plan	Show newcomers how the medical practice will make them known to the community.
Implement a mentor system	Don't choose a mentor who is a superior or subordinate to the physician.
Implement a mentor system for the physician's spouse	Finding someone of the spouse's gender to help him or her adapt to the community is especially important when the physician has relocated.
Integrate into the community	Help the physician and family integrate into the community. Some communities, especially small ones, can be hard to break into, so take extra steps if needed.
Give positive reinforcement	Figure out informal ways to give the newcomer a "pat on the back."
Conduct exit interviews	Interview all physicians who leave. Departing members of the practice can be frank and reveal issues that create difficulty for newcomers.

Many human resource professionals develop a new employee onboarding checklist to ensure that new hires have adjusted to their organization and its culture. There are many different onboarding tool kits available that the practice can customize and use.

Career Development Programs

Career development programs provide opportunities for employees to advance their careers and perform at their highest potential. The most common example of a career development program is supervisory training. These programs are sometimes considered nonessential, but they provide an extra benefit to employees.

Career development programs should be offered within the constraint of the medical practice's needs for higher-level skills and the availability of resources to support these efforts. Devoting time and resources to positively developing staff affects bottom-line results. Career development programs can stimulate employee interest in their jobs, improve overall job performance, and provide management with a broader base to fill vacancies. In addition, employees with an outstanding work record perform better than new recruits.

Academic and Educational Programs

Academic programs often are offered to supplement other types of skills training and career development. They are designed to improve the overall competency in a specific area that may be outside the scope of the employee's present job. Academic and educational programs can be taught by colleges or vocational schools or other training companies either in the classroom or online.

These programs also help employees maintain the essential knowledge and skills necessary for their duties and responsibilities. Employees can lose particular job knowledge and skills if they are not routinely used. Thus academic and education programs can provide an opportunity for employees to reinforce their current skills or discover new skills that will contribute to their competency.

Ethical Standards: The Heart of Professional Responsibility

One of the common threads in all definitions of professionals is adherence to an ethical standard and a definitive statement that individuals will act with integrity. Indeed, some definitions state that the members of a profession will act as ethical enforcement for the rest of the profession. Thus attorneys have membership in their state bar associations as a prerequisite to licensure and launch inquiries and investigations through the bar association when one member accuses another of acting unethically.

Ethical standards require adherence to a higher measure of action than simple, expedient, and technically correct business actions. Ethical behavior requires adherence to duty and vigilance of action. Ethical behavior means actions are not only legal, but correct from a variety of perspectives.

In some cases, ethical behavior may actually increase the costs of doing business, not only from a vigilance perspective, but because actions are taken that would not be made absent an ethical standard. In putting patients' interests above those of the medical practice group, in some cases the practice may come out worse off economically. In treating staff fairly, as opposed to simply what can be gotten away with, a medical practice sometimes will raise its costs. Investing in quality assurance programs because it is the right thing to do for patients can increase a medical practice's costs. Nevertheless, doing the right thing is a cost of doing business and is one that the professionally responsible medical practice executive recognizes.

Medical practices sometimes have competing goals, and if not held to high standards, those so-called structural conflicts can create opportunities for unethical behavior. Maximizing the partners' incomes can compete with goals of serving the community or treating the staff fairly, and it is up to the executive to support that higher standard and recognize and manage the potential conflicts of interest. The professional executive's sense of duty — to patients, partners, staff, and community — is sometimes the last line of defense in guarding against unethical outcomes. In Vermont, a hospital's chief executive officer was sentenced to two years in federal prison for lying to state regulators about the costs of a building expansion. By following his perceived *sole* duty to his employer to get state approval for the project at all costs, he violated ethical principles and even the law. Three others from that hospital's executive team also faced criminal charges in that case.[2]

These types of cases illustrate that maintaining ethical standards is a matter of individual integrity and that only by being bound by a sense of professional responsibility and what is right or wrong will an executive truly rise to the level of a professional.

Professional Networking

Given the complexity of the healthcare environment, the rapid pace of change, and the increasing specialization of the field, the medical practice executive's ability to tap into an informed network of colleagues and organizations is essential. Whether for physicians, allied health professionals, or medical practice leadership, professional organizations exist at all levels — local, regional, national, and even international.

Professional organizations do not have to be limited, however, to the healthcare environment. Groups at the local level, such as Toastmasters, Jaycees, Rotary, and Lions Clubs, offer excellent opportunities to network and participate in the business community at large. MGMA, along with its specialty societies and assemblies, offers opportunities at the state and national levels.

Many an executive's reach has been measured by the power of his or her professional network and ability to reach the right person, at the right place, at the right time. The rise of the Internet and social networking sites has given executives new ways to expand their professional network quickly. Sharing information, experiences, perspectives, and knowledge across a wide network is now literally in the palm of every executive's hand. The power of these networks is undeniable.

Developing Effective Interpersonal Skills

Executives who know themselves will be more effective leaders and will recognize the importance of an interpersonal skill set that values and draws out individual and team contributions. You should have no doubt about the importance of honing your interpersonal skills, as the ability to manage people is a skill set that will ensure your future employment.[3]

Healthcare, by its very nature, is team oriented; indeed, multidisciplinary teams deliver patient care. From the building maintenance staff to the operating room surgeon, scores, if not hundreds, of staff members are involved in the safe and effective delivery of quality healthcare. Collaboration between clinicians and practice professionals, the physician–adminstrator team, is paramount for delivering high-quality patient care.[4] Team management, then, is a critical element in the medical practice executive's success. Effective leadership is the key to developing strong teams, and strong interpersonal skills serve as a foundation for this leadership.[5] Knowledge of team and interpersonal dynamics assists the executive in providing this leadership.

Employee Handbooks

The medical practice needs to communicate its policies, procedures, employee benefits, management and employee responsibilities, and other essential information to all employees. A good way to provide this information is by creating an employee handbook.

An employee handbook typically provides a brief overview of a practice's management philosophy, contains the group's policies, and is distributed to all employees through a printed copy or on the intranet. Together with the practice's policies and procedures manual, the employee handbook contributes to organizational productivity, a competent workforce, and high employee morale. When revisions or additions are made to the policies and procedures, the employee handbook should be updated as necessary so the two reflect the same information.

Benefits of Employee Handbooks

The employee handbook is one of the most important communication tools for both the employer and its employees. It can be used as a marketing and branding tool for current and prospective employees. It is an important management tool and resource document, and it contains employment legal information. Key benefits of developing an employee handbook for the medical practice group are that it:

- Serves as a management tool to communicate the group's policies to employees;
- Allows the practice to highlight its mission, goals, and objectives;
- Provides a marketing opportunity to publicize the group's accomplishments;
- Aids employees to follow established rules; and
- Ensures that all employees receive the same information and that this information is easily accessible.

Employee Handbook Legal Considerations

Sometimes, employee handbooks may be considered enforceable contracts although handbooks should have disclaimers stating they are not contracts. Lawsuits regarding employee handbooks commonly involve breach-of-contract charges in which the employee claims that language in the handbook constituted an offer that the employee accepted. From the charging employee's perspective, this offer and acceptance creates a binding contract between the employer and the employee, which the employer allegedly breached.

One may think that by not having an employee handbook, a medical group will have no contractual obligations. However developing an employee handbook is advisable in today's litigious environment. It is recommended that the medical practice carefully craft, continuously review, and revise its employee handbook to guard against the most troublesome areas that cause the most handbook-related litigation.

Medical practice managers should have every employee sign a disclaimer emphasizing two critical points:

1. Employees are at-will* workers who can be terminated at any time, for any reason or no reason; and
2. The employee handbook is not a contract.

Every employee should sign a disclaimer either during employee orientation or on the first day of work acknowledging the employee handbook was received and read. The signed acknowledgment statement provides essential legal protection for the medical group stating that the employee has read, understood, and agreed to comply with the handbook. A copy of the signed acknowledgment statement should be given back to employees for their records, and the original should be placed in employees' files.

The employment-at-will statement should be one of the first elements in the employee handbook. The acknowledgment statement usually appears as one of the last pages helping to ensure employees do actually read the handbook.

If a medical practice has physical printed copies of the employee handbook, they should be returned to the practice when employment has been terminated.

---

* Check with your legal counsel to ensure the practice is in an at-will state.

Key Elements of Employee Handbooks

The employee handbook should begin with a brief history of the medical practice, its organizational structure, accomplishments, mission, vision, values, and objectives. It is advisable to have a human resource professional help your medical group develop your employee handbook to ensure that employment policies, practices, pay practices, performance evaluations, benefits, and other human resource–related issues are appropriately addressed. The medical group's legal counsel should review the handbook before it is distributed to employees in addition to every time a new policy is created or updated to ensure it complies with all applicable laws. As mentioned earlier, the designated human resource professional should be responsible for periodically updating and revising the handbook as well as informing employees about new changes.

The employee handbook should include:

- Table of contents;
- Welcome letter to employees;
- Introduction;
- Employment at-will statement in states where allowable;
- Medical practice's goals and objectives;
- General working hours and calendar of paid holidays;
- Dress code, customer service, and safety rules;
- Vacation, sick, personal, and other leaves;
- Salary and performance reviews;
- Overtime for nonexempt employees;
- Employee benefits;
- Employee code of conduct and ethics;
- Termination and discipline; and
- A handbook acknowledgment statement for employees to sign.

The employee handbook should have an effective date; contain language indicating that if the handbook is revised, the revised version supersedes all previous handbooks; and include a description of the terms and conditions of employment.

Many medical practices choose to begin with a welcome letter from the administrator or chief executive officer. This letter should make employees feel important and encourage them to contribute to the medical group's goals. It should not state how generous, fair, and excellent the employment package is or how employees can expect a long and happy relationship with the medical practice.

The introduction to the employee handbook should give employees an idea of what it is like to work for the medical group and describe the types of medical services the group provides. It presents the medical practice's mission, vision, values, and history. You may wish to include your code of ethics in this section or present it separately. The introduction should explain that one purpose of the employee handbook is to ensure consistent treatment of employees. It should also explain how to use the employee handbook. You should encourage your employees to read the handbook, become familiar with its contents, and ask questions.

As with all information presented in the employee handbook, your policies on sexual harassment, workplace violence, and nondiscriminatory practices should be expressed simply and briefly. It is not necessary to have the entire policy as it appears in the policies and procedures manual. However, it is imperative if you have both a handbook and a policies and procedures manual that the two documents do not contain any inconsistent or contradictory statements.

The employee benefits section of the employee handbook should briefly describe the benefits offered and include a statement that you retain the right to terminate any benefit plan at any time. You should avoid language that might imply that benefits are entitlements. In addition, you should state that all coverage is subject to terms, restrictions, and other eligibility requirements stated in your plan documents. The employee handbook should indicate how leaves of absence affect leave accrual and the exercise of benefits.

Employee Handbook Checklist

Employee handbooks can be shields or swords depending on their content. To determine the relevance of your handbook and how well it has stood the test of time, answer the following questions and use them as a guide to determine whether revisions in your handbook are warranted.

Does the employee handbook contain any statements indicating that the handbook is a contract? Eliminate any statements that indicate the handbook is a contract. There should be statements throughout your handbook explaining to staff that your handbook only provides information on current policies and procedures. It is not a contract of employment.

Is the employment relationship defined as being *at-will*? The employee handbook should specifically and conspicuously state that the employment relationship is at-will and subject to termination by either party at any time, without stated cause. Such language should appear on the first page and throughout the handbook where appropriate. Review your handbook to ensure that it does not contain language that is inconsistent with that position.

Does the handbook contain a policy regarding workplace harassment that includes a specific complaint procedure? Every employee handbook should state that sexual and other forms of workplace harassment are not tolerated; and retaliation against an employee for making a complaint of discrimination or harassment is strictly prohibited. The statement should list prohibited conduct and outline the procedures for reporting alleged harassment.

Does the handbook contain the words *probationary* or *permanent* when describing employment? Eliminate the words *probationary* and *permanent*. Those words are usually considered to imply that an employee who completes his or her initial period is granted permanent employment and associated benefits. Consequently, you may encounter problems when terminating that employee. Insert language stating that no employee is guaranteed employment for any period of time. Consider words such as *provisionary*, *orientation*, or *introductory* period instead of *probationary* period.

Does the handbook describe the medical group's disciplinary policy? Eliminate or drastically change any required disciplinary steps that may look like progressive discipline is required prior to termination. Any list of inappropriate behaviors or conduct should state that it is not exhaustive. Although it is imperative that you treat all employees consistently, you need the flexibility to terminate an employee on the spot for any reason. Promising to progress through a series of four steps could invite a lawsuit if you fail to follow your own policy.

Does the handbook contain a section on equal employment opportunity, which includes mention of protected classes of people under federal, state, and local laws applicable to the medical group? Be sure that the handbook contains language that the medical practice does not discriminate on the basis of any protected class.

Does the handbook contain language in which fringe *benefits* could be considered fringe *entitlements*? The description of benefits should be accompanied by a statement that the medical group retains the right to end any benefits plan at any time. In addition, the handbook should state that all coverage is subject to the terms, restrictions, and other eligibility requirements stated in your plan documents. Include provisions about how leaves of absence affect leave accrual and the exercise of benefits.

Does the handbook contain an effective date? The employee handbook should contain language that the revised handbook supersedes all previous handbooks and it supersedes any oral and written description of the terms and conditions of employment.

Does the medical group require all employees to sign a statement indicating they have access to and have read the employee handbook and understood all of its provisions? Ensure that your medical practice uses a form to this effect, have employees sign it, give them a copy, and keep one in each employee's file.

Does the handbook state that you have the right to discharge an employee who fails to cooperate with an investigation? Such a statement gives you the right to terminate an employee who refuses to cooperate with an investigation.

Employee Conduct

Certain rules and regulations governing employee behavior are necessary for the orderly operation of your medical practice and for the protection and safety of your employees and patients. These rules and regulations may be outlined in an employee code of conduct. The employee code of conduct is a code of ethical conduct and prescribed behavior. It should clearly specify types of prohibited conduct and indicate that disciplinary action is taken for violations. You should consistently follow and enforce the policy. How individuals act typically depends on how the people in top management act. Your code of conduct policy should be well communicated and reinforced to all staff. These rules should communicate your sincere interest to protect, assist, and guide employees in performing their job duties and responsibilities, especially in how they interact with patients, visitors, and coworkers. A code of conduct can help guide your employees' behaviors and ensure the proper image for the practice.

A code of conduct should state what is expected of employees in general terms. Regulating employee conduct is a matter that should be handled with the utmost sensitivity. Employees should be treated with respect and dignity. Most organizations avoid specific rules that could be seen as too restrictive or unnecessary. A code of conduct should clearly define prohibited conduct. Should the need for disciplinary action arise, your decision will be more readily accepted by employees if a comprehensive conduct policy has been established and communicated to your employees.

Although most organizations have written employment policies and procedures concerning employee conduct, the scope of these policies varies greatly. If an employer chooses to have a code of conduct, it may cover many different areas and depend on the practice's philosophy. A practice's code of conduct may include the following types of topics:

- Absenteeism;
- Employee attitude;
- Business travel;
- Carelessness and negligence;
- Collections of money and gifts;
- Conflicts of interest;
- Coworker relations;
- Destruction or vandalism of property;
- Disorderly conduct;
- Falsification of time cards;
- Fraudulent statements;
- Gambling;
- Gratuities and gifts from patients or vendors;
- Housekeeping;
- Insubordination;
- Intent to harm;

- Personal belongings;
- Maintenance of equipment;
- Media relations;
- Offensive language;
- Patient–employee relations;
- Political activities;
- Professional organizations;
- Stealing and embezzling; and
- Personal visitors.

Complying with Employment Laws and Regulatory Standards

Human resource policies provide a framework for both the medical practice and the employee. These policies allow the medical practice to direct its employee relations and articulate what is expected, and the policies should prevent any misunderstandings about employer policies.

Employees often do not know their rights and responsibilities and may receive bad advice from coworkers or friends. An employee handbook that spells out the medical practice's procedures and policies can help provide each employee with guidance on what is considered an acceptable action and well within the law.

Smaller medical practices may not have the range of written policies and procedures that a larger practice has. Regardless of practice size, the medical practice executive is responsible for ensuring that all appropriate laws and regulations are observed and followed. Failure to do so may result in inconsistent and noncompliant conduct and cause for a potential lawsuit.

Employment law is complex and requires a keen awareness to ensure compliance. A medical group executive may need support from an attorney or human resource consultant to ensure compliance with all appropriate laws. A periodic external review of current practices to ensure compliance with the law will demonstrate a commitment toward compliance. Written policies should be reviewed by legal counsel to ensure that they reflect applicable federal, state, and local requirements.

Well-run medical groups will be up to date on the various labor relations issues that may affect them. Whether this is done through an experienced human resource professional, outside legal counsel, or the medical practice executive's own efforts, all of those in managerial positions should be knowledgeable on a range of issues, from requirements on minimum wage, workers' compensation, and unemployment compensation, to unions, collective bargaining, and fair employment practices.

Regulating Government Departments and Agencies

The U.S. Department of Labor (DOL) and the Equal Employment Opportunity Commission (EEOC) enforce the federal employment laws. These mandates and the regulations that implement them cover many workplace activities for most employers and workers.

The DOL enforces laws and regulations covering:

- Wages and hours;
- Occupational safety and health;
- Workers' compensation (for federal employees);
- Employee benefit plans;
- Unions and their members;
- Employee protection;
- Uniformed service members employment and reemployment rights;
- Employee polygraph protection;
- Whistleblower and retaliation protection;
- Garnishment of wages;
- Family and medical leave; and
- Immigrant workers.

Some state and local labor laws differ from the federal laws. Be sure to keep up to date not only with federal labor laws but also with your state and local laws.

The other government agency with significant effect on employment law is the EEOC. It regulates and enforces federal Equal Employment Opportunity (EEO) laws and discriminatory practices. The EEOC pinpoints many types of discrimination, including the following:

- Age;
- Disability;
- Equal pay and compensation;
- Genetic information;
- National origin;
- Pregnancy;
- Race and color;
- Religion;
- Retaliation;
- Sex; and
- Sexual harassment.

These laws underscore the importance of avoiding any form of discrimination within your medical practice. They affect nearly every human resource management policy that you develop and implement. *Discriminatory practice* means that it is illegal to discriminate in any aspect of employment, including the following:

- Hiring and firing;
- Compensation, assignment, or classification of employees;
- Transfer, promotion, layoff, or recall;
- Job advertisements;
- Recruitment;
- Testing;
- Use of company facilities;
- Training and apprenticeship programs;
- Fringe benefits;
- Retirement plans;
- Disability leave; and
- Other terms and conditions of employment.

Training and Development Laws and Regulations

Antidiscrimination laws cover employee training and development as well as other employment practices. Title VII of the Civil Rights Act of 1964, as amended, prohibits covered employers from discriminating against employees based on race, color, religion, sex, or national origin with respect to training and development. Additional federal, state, and local laws may prohibit discrimination in training and development based on additional protected categories, such as sexual orientation. However, employers are allowed to put some restrictions on employee training. For example, a training session may be limited to only employees who possess certain skills, have passed a certain exam, or who have demonstrated exceptional competence based on work history and performance.

The Fair Labor Standards Act of 1938 (FLSA) specifies that attendance at lectures, meetings, training programs, and similar activities must be counted as compensable working time unless the following criteria are met:

- Attendance is outside of the employee's regular working hours;
- Attendance is voluntary;
- The training is not job related; and
- The employee does not perform any work during such attendance.

General Regulations

Specific laws involving employment are discussed later in the chapter. The following is an overview of some general regulations to consider when running a practice.

Wages and benefits. From a legal perspective, the medical practice follows the federal FLSA, which requires a minimum wage of $7.25 per hour. The FLSA also requires equal pay for equal work regardless of gender. Some states have enacted higher minimum wage requirements, but most medical practices pay employees more than the minimum wage.

A medical practice may not restrict benefits for employees of a like group. Benefits must be administered fairly and consistently. For example, if health insurance is available for full-time nonexempt staff, a medical practice may not indicate that one medical receptionist may have health insurance and another one cannot because that employee has insurance with a spouse. The benefit must be offered to all eligible employees. It is up to employees to determine whether they want, or are even eligible for, that benefit.

Performance reviews. Performance or lack of performance and how that evaluation is communicated with the employee could result in an unsatisfied employee. If the employee can demonstrate that the performance review is discriminatory or has violated a certain law, the medical group must be confident that its practices and process comply with the law.

Many lawsuits surround employees contesting a disciplinary action process that results in termination. It is critical that the medical practice have a written process that is consistent with the law and is administered fairly and consistently.

Safety and health. Every medical practice must keep its employees safe from harm. The physician credo to "do no harm" to the patient must be extended to the employee in the workplace. The medical practice executive should work diligently toward employee and patient safety. The group practice environment must be safe and comply with OSHA laws as well as with local zoning or building codes.

Fraud and abuse. The U.S. Office of Inspector General carries out a broad range of duties nationally through audits, investigations, and inspections to protect the U.S. Department of Health and Human Services programs and the beneficiaries of those programs. It has developed guidelines for individual and small medical practices toward the development and implementation of a voluntary compliance program that promotes adherence to any and all federal healthcare program requirements.

Every medical practice has a duty and responsibility to ensure that its physicians and employees are knowledgeable and committed to following the rules and regulations of the federal government and that they know what those rules are. The guidelines include the following:

- Designating a compliance officer;
- Implementing compliance through written and well-communicated standards;
- Having medical practice–specific education and training;

- Communicating appropriately with employees, physicians, and others;
- Performing internal monitoring and auditing;
- Responding to compliance issues with appropriate corrective action; and
- Enforcing sanctions for noncompliance.

Nondiscrimination. Medical practices may have a nondiscrimination statement that prohibits discrimination in all of its activities on the basis of certain classes such as race, color, national origin, sex, religion, age, disability, sexual orientation, and marital or family status. Persons with disabilities who require other means for medical practice communication information, such as interpretation services, should contact the medical practice executive. Also, the medical practice executive should offer the person the ability to file a complaint of discrimination by providing an address and/or telephone number for the person to contact, if warranted. The medical practice usually would provide a statement in its internal publications that states "ABC Medical Practice is an equal opportunity provider and employer."

Payroll records. Every medical group needs to keep records on its payroll practices. Based on the common saying, "If it's not documented, it wasn't done," medical groups need to have employees record the hours worked in the group practice. Payroll procedures and policies should be established to ensure that a fair, consistent, and legal process is followed in paying employees the correct amount for the exact hours worked.

There are particular laws that govern payroll practices, including that nonsalaried employees are to be compensated for overtime and that time cards are properly completed and signed off by employees. In many organizations, inaccurately completed time cards can result in termination.

Employment-at-will. The concept of employment-at-will, or the ability of employers to dismiss an at-will employee for any reason and at any time, continues to be difficult because many employment protections enacted into law, court rulings, and state statutes have limited employers' rights to terminate employees at will. Employees can claim wrongful discharge and sue for damages if the discharge results from a broken promise made by the employer (oral, written, or implied) or a violation of public policy.

More than 30 states recognize some exceptions to the employment-at-will doctrine. If an employer terminates an employee for a reason determined to be an exception to the at-will doctrine, that termination constitutes an unjust dismissal and, consequently, that employee can receive damages or reinstatement.

Your medical group practice should focus on human resource management policies that provide effective guidelines to promote consistency of management rather than emphasizing the limitation on employment-at-will. Documentation of these policies is important, including a human resource manual that presents clear policies, especially those related to progressive discipline and termination.

Your employee handbook should include a statement related to employment-at-will.

Avoiding Wrongful Discharge Actions

Today in medical practices, immediate terminations caused by gross misconduct tend to be rare. Many terminations are performance related and preventable if selection, orientation, training, supervision, coaching, and discipline practices are conducted effectively. Proactive performance management can help protect your medical practice from wrongful discharge actions and unwarranted unemployment insurance claims. Some measures that will reduce the risk of liability include the following:

- **Develop a written policy that covers the grounds for termination.** Like all policies, this one should be communicated to all employees through an employee handbook, the human resource policies and procedures manual, and on the medical group's intranet. This step may help protect against charges of termination without proper warning.
- **Use clear and precise language, including terminology, when developing policies and procedures.** Solicit your legal counsel to review the language in all of your medical practice's policies.

- **Include specific disclaimers** on job application forms, policy materials, and employee handbooks, explaining that these documents do not constitute an employee contract.
- **Educate managers about the importance of logging and documenting every termination action.** Managers should keep precise records of training and retraining, coaching, performance improvement action plans and results, probationary and warning notices, remedial efforts, and other actions taken that should precede any termination action. The human resource department should help the managers keep these records.
- **Ensure that the practice's performance review forms and job descriptions accurately reflect the performance expected in job-related specific terms** (e.g., objectives and behaviors) and are used by all managers to document each employee's strong and weak performance points. Managers must understand that they must write examples of behaviors that justify their ratings on the performance review forms. A common mistake is giving employees favorable annual performance review assessments and then terminating them.
- **Reinforce to managers the importance of warning employees in advance when their actions could possibly lead to termination unless significant changes occur in their performance.** These warnings should be documented in writing or have witnesses in attendance during an oral conversation (over the phone or in person).
- **Train managers to stay alert for signs of poor performance,** such as decreased productivity, baseless complaints, and increased absenteeism and tardiness. Human resource professionals should help managers assist their direct reports through a committed effort to coaching, retraining, and concentrating on the specifics of successful performance.
- **Communicate to managers frequently and effectively that termination of an employee is not solely their decision.** The decision to terminate an employee must involve others (e.g., the supervisor's manager and a designated human resource professional) to ensure that an employee cannot allege malice or

personality conflict on the part of the supervisor. Consult your legal counsel or employers' council if a termination case appears to be complex and problematic. In addition, establish a procedure that only designated supervisors and managers are authorized to express and make oral and written hiring decisions.

- **Consider establishing a severance package that includes limited-time continuation of health and life insurance benefits.** Such a courtesy may preclude any charges of vindictiveness and may help mollify any injured feelings. Terminated employees who consider severance payments generous are less likely to initiate litigation, and the costs are typically much less than legal expenses.
- **Consider purchasing defense and judgment insurance** that protects employees against lawsuits arising from cases other than personal injury or property-damages suits, which are covered under general liability policies.
- **Keep in mind that federal law protects employees against retaliation** for raising certain concerns about a healthcare provider's compliance with health information privacy laws and laws intended to prevent waste, fraud, and abuse in healthcare. Termination decisions must not violate applicable nonretaliation laws.
- **Conduct training for managers and supervisors on their responsibilities and employee rights,** particularly those related to discipline and termination.
- **Terminate employees only as a last resort and with great care and compassion.** The exit interview should be isolated from other employees to avoid embarrassment for the person, as well as to avoid upsetting and distracting other employees. The reasons for termination should be explained clearly. If the supervisor, manager, and designated human resource professional have followed the appropriate pretermination steps, the termination should be no surprise to the employee. Termination can create ripples in the medical practice that go far beyond legal consideration, so handle all terminations with sensitivity.

State and Local Laws on Sexual Orientation

Sexual orientation laws have been developed by some states and localities, but not federally. A medical practice should be fully aware of its state laws and the respective requirements placed on the employer. In New York, for example, the Sexual Orientation Non-Discrimination Act of 2002 prohibits discrimination on the basis of actual or perceived sexual orientation in employment, housing, public accommodations, education, credit, and the exercise of civil rights. This latter protected category was newly added to various state laws, including New York's Human Rights Law, Civil Rights Law, and Education Law.

Although a medical practice may choose to follow a certain law even if it isn't required in its particular location, it must follow those laws and their administration in those states where it does apply. This involves the medical practice executive knowing not just that the state law exists, but also how it is interpreted and implemented in that state. Usually, when a law is passed, numerous legal firms and human resource consultants are available to provide advice on how to follow the new law.

Licensure and Certification

Certain medical professions require licensure or certification. The medical practice executive should ensure that the affected employees are appropriately licensed or certified and that their licenses are updated accordingly. For example, a physician's medical license is state-specific and requires renewal on a periodic basis.

The medical practice executive needs to keep the physician's updated medical license on file because that is a requirement for employment. Failure to do so could result in a medical provider administering care without a license and the concomitant sanctions against the practice for allowing the provider to do so.

Record-Keeping

Keeping accurate and timely employee records and files is necessary to maintain a well-run practice. From updated addresses and emergency contacts to completed tax forms and signed disciplinary action paperwork, the medical practice executive should provide diligent maintenance of employee records. Practical issues follow if the records are not kept up to date.

In an emergency situation in which the medical practice building is without electrical power and the practice will be closed, employees need to be informed of the closure. If telephone numbers are not updated, a problem exists for contacting employees in a timely manner. Personnel records must also be up to date in case of a medical problem with an employee, such as fainting while on the job; without current records, it may take life-saving time to determine the possible reason for the fainting, such as an insulin attack.

Specific Legislation

The following is a discussion of particular employment-related laws. These laws are referenced as they are written and understood at the time of this book printing. Check with your legal counsel, state and local government agencies, and the MGMA Government Affairs office for recent updates and changes to these laws.

Americans with Disabilities Act of 1990

The Americans with Disabilities Act (ADA) prohibits private employers, state and local governments, employment agencies, and labor unions from discriminating against qualified individuals with disabilities in job application procedures, hiring, firing, advancement, compensation, job training, and other employment aspects. The ADA covers employers with 15 or more employees. An individual with a disability, defined as a protected individual, is a person who has a physical or mental impairment that substantially limits one or more major life activities, has a record of such impairment, or is regarded as having such impairment.

Not every disabled individual is protected under the ADA; the person must also be qualified. A *qualified* employee or applicant with a disability is an individual who, with or without reasonable accommodation, can perform the essential functions of the job in question. *Essential functions*, as presented in well-written job descriptions, are those functions that are essential to performance of the position in question. To determine whether a function is essential, examine whether:

- **The position exists to perform the function.** For example, positions involving phone responses can reasonably require that the employee be able to hear and speak if he or she will be assessing whether in-coming calls are emergent, urgent, or nonemergent.
- **Only a limited number of other employees are available to perform the function.** For example, an essential function for a file clerk may be to answer the phone only if two employees are in a very busy office and they all handle a variety of tasks.
- **The function is highly specialized and the person is hired for his or her special expertise or ability to perform the function.** For example, fluency in Spanish is an essential expertise or ability to perform the function to communicate with Spanish-speaking patients.

Qualified individuals do not include job applicants or employees engaging in illegal use of drugs when the individual's usage is the basis for an employer's actions. For example, an employer terminates an employee for coming to work high on drugs and not being able to complete essential functions. The terminated employee would not be considered a qualified individual under the ADA.

Under the ADA, discrimination may include limiting or classifying a job applicant or employee in an adverse way, denying employment opportunities or promotions to people who qualify, or not making reasonable accommodations to the known physical or mental limitations of disabled employees. Reasonable accommodations may include, but are not limited to:

- Making existing facilities readily accessible to and usable by persons with disabilities. This accessibility is particularly important to healthcare providers because they are considered public accommodations under Title III of the ADA.
- Job restructuring; modifying work schedules; reassigning the employee to a vacant position; acquiring or modifying equipment or devices; adjusting or modifying exams, training materials, or policies; and providing qualified readers or interpreters.

Reasonable accommodations by the employer are limited only if they are an "undue hardship" on its operations. Undue hardship is defined as an action that requires "significant difficulty or expense"[6] in relation to the size of the employing organization, the resources available, and the nature of the operation.

Title V of the ADA protects individuals from coercion, intimidation, threat, harassment, interference, and retaliation in the exercise of their own rights or their encouragement of someone else's exercise of rights granted by the ADA. The EEOC enforces ADA complaints and claims.

The ADA Amendments Act of 2008 (ADAAA) effectively amended the ADA to broaden and clarify the definition of *disability*. It was also designed to strike a balance between employer and employee interests that had been upset through various U.S. Supreme Court rulings and EEOC regulations. A major change was that the ADAAA prohibits the consideration of a mitigating measure, such as medication, assistive technology, accommodations, or modifications, when determining if an impairment substantially limits a major life activity. This includes impairments that are episodic or in remission. The ADAAA also more fully defines what a major life activity is. According to the amendment, a *major life activity* includes but is not limited to:

- Caring for oneself;
- Performing manual tasks;
- Seeing, hearing, speaking, and breathing;
- Eating and sleeping;
- Walking, standing, bending, and lifting; and
- Learning, reading, concentrating, thinking, communicating, and working.

Also included in this list are major bodily functions such as functions of the immune system; normal cell growth; and digestive, bowel, bladder, neurological, brain, respiratory, circulatory, endocrine, and reproductive functions.

The Family and Medical Leave Act of 1993

The Family and Medical Leave Act (FMLA) requires covered employers to provide up to 12 weeks of unpaid, job-protected leave to eligible employees for certain family and medical reasons. Medical practice employees are eligible if they have worked for the medical practice for more than one year, for 1,250 hours over the previous 12 months, and if there are at least 50 employees within the medical group within 75 miles of the practice's main office (some employees may work off-site or at satellite clinics, but these must be within a 75-mile radius). In addition, the FMLA allows employees to take leave on an intermittent basis or to work a reduced schedule under certain circumstances.

This far-reaching legislation has tremendous employment impact for larger medical groups with more than 50 employees but does not affect smaller medical groups. By being legally required to hold a person's job for up to 12 weeks, the larger medical practice is challenged to find adequate and appropriate coverage during this time frame.

Many states have enacted laws with additional mandates to the FMLA. These extra mandates include FMLA compliance for organizations with fewer employees and an expanded definition of the immediate family, including domestic partners and their children, grandparents, and in-laws. Ensure that your medical practice is in compliance with your state's mandates.

Occupational Safety and Health Act of 1970

The Occupational Safety and Health (OSH) Act protects employees from harm on the job and has established a nationwide, federal program to protect the workforce from job-related death, injury, and illness. OSHA was developed within the DOL to administer the OSH Act. The OSH Act significantly affects medical practices, especially in the areas of responsibility that include policies on blood-borne pathogens, emergency response, hearing safety, lockout-tagout, respiratory safety, lead safety, fire safety, office ergonomics, personal protective equipment, material safety data sheets, and right-to-know for hazard communication materials. OSHA focuses on three strategies:

1. Strong, fair, and effective enforcement, especially of the most hazardous industries (those with high injury and illness rates);
2. Outreach, education, and compliance assistance; and
3. Partnerships and cooperative programs.

A medical practice must be fully aware and compliant with OSHA regulations at the workplace. Complying with OSHA will help to provide employees with a safe work environment.

Consolidated Omnibus Budget Reconciliation Act of 1985

The Consolidated Omnibus Budget Reconciliation Act (COBRA) provides certain former employees, retirees, spouses, former spouses, and dependent children the right to temporary continuation of health coverage at group rates. This coverage is only available when coverage is lost due to certain specific events.

Group health coverage for COBRA participants is typically more expensive than health coverage for current employees. Usually, the employer pays a part of the premium for current employees while COBRA participants generally pay the entire premium themselves.

Employee Polygraph Protection Act of 1988

The Employee Polygraph Protection Act generally prevents employers from using polygraph tests, either for preemployment screening or during the course of employment, with certain exemptions. Employers usually may not require or request any employee or job applicant to take a polygraph test, or discharge, discipline, or discriminate against an employee or job applicant for refusing to take a test or for tests to be administered to certain job applicants in certain industries (such as security services and pharmaceuticals) and those reasonably suspected of involvement in a workplace incident (such as theft and embezzlement) that results in specific economic loss or injury to the employer. When polygraph tests are allowed, they are subject to strict standards.

Employee Retirement Income Security Act of 1974

The Employee Retirement Income Security Act (ERISA) regulates employers who offer pensions or welfare benefit plans to their employees. Title I of ERISA is administered by the Employee Benefits Security Administration and imposes a wide range of fiduciary, disclosure, and reporting requirements on fiduciaries of pension and welfare benefit plans and on others having dealings with these plans. ERISA does not require employers to provide pensions or health or other welfare benefit plans; however, it regulates those plans once established by an organization. ERISA has been amended several times, including by the Pension Protection Act of 2006; the Worker, Retiree, and Employer Recovery Act of 2008; COBRA as mentioned earlier; the Newborns' and Mothers' Health Protection Act of 1996; the Mental Health Parity Act of 1996; the Women's Health and Cancer Rights Act of 1998; and HIPAA.

Health Insurance Portability and Accountability Act of 1996

HIPAA is regulated by the Employee Benefits Security Administration. Although much of the focus of this act, especially in healthcare organizations, has been on the accountability for ensuring patient privacy and confidentiality, the act's original emphasis was on the portability of insurance benefits. Title I of HIPAA protects health insurance coverage for workers and their families when they change or lose their jobs. In particular, the act gives the employee protection in terms of existing health conditions. HIPAA also requires healthcare providers to submit certain electronic transactions related to healthcare payment, such as authorizations and claims submissions, in standard formats.

Patient Protection and Affordable Care Act and Health Care and Education Reconciliation Act of 2010

The Patient Protection and Affordable Care Act (PPACA) and the Health Care and Education Reconciliation Act amending the PPACA were signed into law on March 23 and 30, 2010, respectively.

Employers with more than 50 employees face tax penalties if they do not provide all full-time employees affordable health coverage. If an employer does not follow this mandate, tax penalties will be imposed on a per-employee basis. Provisions in the PPACA will help some eligible small healthcare organizations (those with fewer than 25 employees) that provide health insurance to their employees through subsidies and various tax credits. These subsidies will expire several years after the establishment of health insurance exchanges in each state by 2014. The health insurance exchanges are a marketplace for individuals and small businesses to shop for health insurance plans at a competitive price.

The PPACA also enacted changes to reimbursable expenditures on an employee's health flexible spending account (FSA), health savings account (HSA), or health reimbursable arrangement. Over-the-counter drugs are no longer reimbursable unless they are prescribed by a physician (except for insulin). Also, the penalty for employees who make withdrawals from their HSAs for nonmedical purposes increased to 20 percent. Employee FSA contributions were set at a maximum of $2,500 per employee, and increased to $2,550 per employee in 2015.

The PPACA also will affect payroll and taxable deductions. The acts increase the employee portion of the Medicare tax by an additional

0.9 percent for individuals with an annual income over $200,000 or a household annual income over $250,000. This additional tax is levied on the combined wages of the employee and the employee's spouse in the case of a joint tax filing. Employers are required to withhold this additional tax similar to the existing Medicare (the Hospital Insurance) payroll tax. This provision applies to wages received after December 31, 2012.

The PPACA also codifies many of wellness program provisions from HIPAA. According to the PPACA, employers may establish wellness programs providing a minimum discount, rebate, or other reward for participation without violating any antidiscrimination rules for group health plans based on health status–related factors. The wellness incentive was increased to 30 percent of the cost of coverage in the PPACA.

Title VII of the Civil Rights Acts of 1964

Title VII of the Civil Rights Act protects individuals against employment discrimination on the basis of race, color, sex, national origin, and religion. Title VII also protects individuals because of an association with another individual of a particular race, color, sex, national origin, or religion. This means that an employer cannot discriminate against a person because of his or her interracial association with another person, such as an interracial marriage. It applies to employers with 15 or more employees. In 2012, the EEOC ruled that employment discrimination on the basis of gender identity or transgender status is also prohibited under Title VII.

In terms of race and color discrimination, Title VII states that equal employment opportunity cannot be denied to any person because of his or her racial group or perceived racial group or his or her other race-linked characteristics (such as hair texture, color, and/or facial features). It prohibits employment decisions based on stereotypes and assumptions about abilities, traits, or the performance of individuals of certain ethnicities. These prohibitions apply to all races, colors, and ethnicities.

All employees and job applicants, regardless of their nation of origin, are entitled to the same employment opportunities. National origin discrimination means treating persons less favorably because they come from a particular place, because of their ethnicity or accent, or because it is believed that they have a particular ethnic background.

Under Title VII, it is unlawful to discriminate because of gender against any employee or job applicant in hiring, termination, promotion, compensation, job training, or any other term, condition, or privilege or employment. Title VII also prohibits employment decisions based on stereotypes and assumptions about abilities, traits, or the performance of individuals on the basis of sex. It prohibits both intentional discrimination and neutral job policies that disproportionately exclude individuals on the basis of sex and that are not job related. Title VII's prohibitions against sex-based discrimination also cover sexual harassment and pregnancy-based discrimination.

Sexual harassment is a form of sex discrimination that violates Title VII. Unwelcome sexual advances, requests for sexual favors, and other verbal or physical conduct of a sexual nature constitute sexual harassment, when this conduct explicitly or implicitly affects an individual's employment, unreasonably interferes with an individual's work performance, or creates an intimidating, hostile, or offensive work environment. A *hostile workplace* is defined as an environment where any type of EEO-related harassment occurs.

The Pregnancy Discrimination Act of 1978 amended the Civil Rights Act, stating that discrimination on the basis of pregnancy, childbirth, or related medical conditions constitutes unlawful sex discrimination under Title VII. Women who are pregnant or affected by related conditions must be treated in the same manner as other applicants or employees with similar abilities or limitations. When hiring, an employer cannot refuse to hire a pregnant woman because of her pregnancy, a pregnancy-related condition, or the prejudices of coworkers, clients, or customers. In terms of pregnancy and maternity leave, an employer may not single out pregnancy-related conditions for special procedures to determine an employee's ability to work.

Title VII also prohibits employers from discriminating against individuals because of their religion in hiring, firing, and other terms and conditions of employment. Employers may not treat employees or applicants more or less favorably because of their religious beliefs or practices, except to the extent a religious accommodation is warranted. Employees cannot be forced to participate, or not participate, in a religious activity as a condition of employment. Employers must reasonably accommodate employees' sincerely held practices unless doing so would impose an undue hardship on the employer.

An employer may not fire, demote, harass, or otherwise retaliate against an individual for filing a charge of discrimination, participating in a discrimination proceeding, or otherwise opposing discrimination. The same laws that prohibit discrimination also prohibit retaliation against individuals who oppose unlawful discrimination or participate in an employment discrimination proceeding.

Executive Order 10925 of 1961, signed by President John F. Kennedy,[7] was the first time the term *affirmative action* was used regarding workplace discrimination against race, color, and national origin ensuring that protected applicants were employed and treated equally. In 1967, Executive Order 11375, signed by President Lyndon B. Johnson,[8] added sex discrimination to the definition of affirmative action. The purpose of these executive orders was to pressure employers into the compliance with the Civil Rights Act of 1964. Keep in mind that some states, such as California, Michigan, and Washington, have constitutional amendments banning affirmative action within these states.

The EEOC, which was created by Title VII, enforces the Civil Rights Act. The Equal Employment Opportunity Act of 1972 strengthened the EEOC by giving it the authority to institute legal action if conciliation fails in disputes involving employment discrimination. It extended the antidiscrimination provisions of Title VII of the Civil Rights Act to educational institutions and state and local governments.

Consumer Credit Protection Act of 1968

Title III of the Consumer Credit Protection Act (CCPA) is enforced by the Wage and Hour Division of the DOL and protects employees from discharge by their employers because their wages have been garnished for any debt. The CCPA also sets limits on the amount of an employee's earnings that may be garnished in any one week. Title III is informally known as the *Federal Wage Garnishment Law*.

Immigration Reform and Control Act of 1986

The Immigration Reform and Control Act (IRCA) requires employers to hire only persons who may legally work in the United States, that is, U.S. citizens, noncitizen nationals, lawful permanent residents, and aliens authorized to work in the United States. The employer must verify the identity and employment eligibility of anyone to be hired, which includes completing the Employment Eligibility Verification Form (Form I-9).

To avoid discrimination problems, an employer should not ask for documentation until after a job offer is extended. Employers must keep each I-9 form on file at least three years or one year after employment ends, whichever is longer.

The IRCA prohibits employers from knowingly hiring, recruiting, or referring for work aliens who are not authorized to accept employment in the United States. Knowing includes not only actual knowledge but also constructive knowledge, that is, information that may fairly be inferred through notice of certain facts and circumstances that would lead a person to know about a certain condition. Inference cannot be based on a person's appearance or accent.

Uniformed Services Employment and Reemployment Rights Act of 1994

The Uniformed Services Employment and Reemployment Rights Act ensures that certain persons who serve in the armed forces have a right to reemployment with the employer they were with when they entered the service for five years of active duty. These persons include those called up from the reserves or National Guard. It also prohibits discrimination based on military service or obligation including returning disabled veterans.

These rights are administered by the Veterans' Employment and Training Service. Employers are required to report annually the organization's employment of veterans.

National Labor Relations Act of 1935 (Wagner Act) and Taft–Hartley Act

The Wagner Act guarantees the right of employees to organize and bargain collectively through representatives of their own choice. It requires employers to bargain in good faith with recognized unions, and it created the National Labor Relations Board to administer the act.

The Labor-Management Relations Act of 1947 (Taft–Hartley Act) effectively amended the Wagner Act. The Taft–Hartley Act sought to balance the power of labor unions and management by prohibiting certain unfair labor practices by unions, by protecting the individual worker's position from union coercion, and by regulating union officers.

Labor-Management Reporting and Disclosure Act of 1959 (Landrum–Griffin Act)

The Labor-Management Reporting and Disclosure Act or Landrum–Griffin Act established a so-called bill of rights for labor union members and strengthened provisions of the Taft–Hartley Act regulating internal union practices. The Landrum–Griffin Act was designed to stop corrupt practices and protect law-abiding unions.

Fair Labor Standards Act of 1938

The FLSA, as amended, established minimum wages, outlawed child labor, and established overtime pay, equal pay, and record-keeping affecting more than 50 million full-time and part-time workers. Some employees are exempt from FLSA, including professional white-collar workers. *Exempt* means these employees, including professional, administrative, and executive employees, are not eligible for overtime pay. To be considered exempt, employees must be paid at least $455 per week and perform duties:

- Involving the management and/or general business operations of the organization;
- Requiring specialized academic training;
- In a computer field; or
- Selling the organization's services outside the place of business.

Exemptions are determined on a case-by-case basis, and job titles do not alone determine exemptions. Nonexempt employees are eligible for overtime pay in the event that they work more than 12 hours in a workday or if they work more than 40 hours in a workweek.

For example, consider whether an employee with the job title of *nurse* is exempt or nonexempt. To qualify for the *learned professional* employee exemption, all of the following requirements must be met:

- The employee must be compensated on a salary or fee basis (as defined in the regulations) at a rate not less than $455 per week;
- The employee's primary duty must be the performance of work requiring advanced knowledge, defined as work that is predominantly intellectual in character and that includes work requiring the consistent exercise of discretion and judgment;

- The advanced knowledge must be in a field of science or learning; and
- The advanced knowledge must be customarily acquired by a prolonged course of specialized intellectual instruction.

Registered nurses who are paid on an hourly basis should receive overtime pay. However, registered nurses who are registered by the appropriate state examining board generally meet the duties requirements for the learned professional exemption, and if paid on a salary basis of at least $455 per week, may be classified as exempt.

Licensed practical nurses and other similar healthcare employees, however, generally do not qualify as exempt learned professionals, regardless of work experience and training, because possession of a specialized advanced academic degree is not a standard prerequisite for entry into such occupations, and they are entitled to overtime pay.

FLSA particularly focuses on ensuring that employees do receive minimum wage and overtime back wages. The Wage and Hour Division sternly enforces these provisions.

Equal Pay Act of 1963

The Equal Pay Act amended the FLSA and is enforced by the EEOC. It prohibits sex-based wage discrimination between men and women in the same medical practice who perform duties under similar working conditions.

If a court finds that the practice is in violation of this law, the judge can fine the group up to $10,000 and/or send the responsible party (e.g., the owner or the medical practice executive) to jail for up to six months. Gender should not be taken into consideration when paying an employee for work done in the medical practice.

Age Discrimination in Employment Act of 1967

The Age Discrimination in Employment Act (ADEA) protects individuals who are 40 years of age or older from employment discrimination based on age, and it applies to both employees and job applicants. It was amended in 1986 to prohibit mandatory retirement. Under the ADEA, it is unlawful to discriminate against a person because of his or her age with respect to any term, condition, or privilege of employment, including hiring, firing, promotion, layoff, compensation, benefits, job assignments, and training.

The ADEA applies to employers with 20 or more employees. Employers can still discharge an employee regardless of his or her age for legitimate, nondiscriminatory reasons. In addition, the ADEA has an exception that allows employers to discriminate on the basis of age for safety reasons, which is referred to as a *bona fide occupational qualification.*

An employer can ask an employee to waive his or her rights or claims under the ADEA either in the settlement of an ADEA administrative or court claim or in connection with an exit incentive program or other employment termination program. There are specific minimum standards that must be met in order for a waiver to be considered by the courts as knowing and voluntary and, thereby, valid. Finally, employers have the right to offer *voluntary* retirement incentives to employees.

The EEOC has adopted *Uniform Guidelines on Employee Selection Procedures* ensuring that selection procedures are consistent with applicable discrimination laws. The basic principle of the *Uniform Guidelines on Employee Selection Procedures* is a that a selection process including employment tests that adversely affect the employment of protected individuals and thus disproportionately selects them out of the recruitment process is unlawful unless the process abides by the guidelines.

Older Workers Benefit Protection Act of 1990

The Older Workers Benefit Protection Act (OWBPA) prohibits age discrimination in employee benefits. It also established the minimum standards for determining the validity of waivers of claims under the ADEA. The OWBPA requires employers offering group exit programs to provide notice of individuals covered and any time limitations. It also prohibits employers from denying employee benefits to older workers based on age.

Genetic Information Nondiscrimination Act of 2008

Title II of the Genetic Information Nondiscrimination Act (GINA) prohibits employers from discriminating based on an individual's genetic information when making hiring, firing, job placement, or promotion decisions with respect to compensation, terms, conditions, or privileges of employment. Genetic information as defined by GINA is an individual's genetic tests, the genetic tests of the individual's family members, the predisposition of a disease or disorder in the individual or family members, and the individual's medical history.

GINA also prohibits employers from requesting, requiring, or purchasing genetic information from an employee, job applicant, or family members except if the employee volunteers the information for services such as part of a wellness program. Employers can ask for medical history when required by family and medical leaves, for law enforcement purposes, or for reasons regarding workplace safety.

GINA also requires employers who have access to employee's genetic information to ensure confidentiality of such information. The information should be kept on separate forms and in separate files from personnel records. They should be treated as a confidential medical records under HIPAA regulations.

Vocational Rehabilitation Act

In 1917, the U.S. Congress passed the Smith–Hughes Vocational Education Act, promoting states to give rehabilitation services to disabled veterans, which was the first of several pieces of legislation enacted to provide training and rehabilitation services to disabled veterans and civilians. Later legislation expanded the services and those eligible to receive them.

National vocational rehabilitation programs now operate under the authority of the Department of Veterans Affairs and the U.S. Department of Education. Medical practice executives can work with agencies to determine how they can help support this program, including ways to provide potential candidates with jobs.[9]

Vietnam-Era Veterans' Readjustment Assistance Act of 1974

The Vietnam-Era Veterans' Readjustment Assistance Act requires that employers with federal contracts or subcontracts of $25,000 or more provide equal opportunity for Vietnam-era veterans, special disabled veterans, and certain veterans who served on active duty. Although this law may not apply to medical practices, the medical group must be aware of the circumstances under which it may apply.

Pregnancy Discrimination Act of 1978

The Pregnancy Discrimination Act indicates that discrimination on the basis of pregnancy, childbirth, or related medical conditions is unlawful under Title VII of the Civil Rights Act. A pregnant woman should be evaluated regarding her ability or inability to work and should not be terminated, be refused employment, or, conversely, be promoted because of a pregnancy.

Affirmative Action

Affirmative action is the set of public policies designed to help eliminate discrimination based on race, color, religion, sex, or national origin. The medical practice executive can request that all potential employees complete forms indicating their backgrounds, which are independently summarized to demonstrate that the practice is considering all potential candidates regardless of race, color, religion, sex, or national origin. Sometimes a practice will list that it is an affirmative action employer to demonstrate its commitment to diversity.

Communicating Laws and Regulations to Employees

Clear and concise policies and procedures documented in an employee handbook, a policies and procedures manual, and/or on your medical practice's intranet will help you and your staff's ability to comply with employment laws and regulations.

Many of the laws and regulations previously mentioned have provisions requiring posters to be visible by all employees. Some medical practices have a bulletin board in the human resource departments for these posters. Others put them in the employee break area or in other areas where there is considerable employee traffic. Each state has slightly different requirements, so be sure to check with your state to determine which posters must be visible at your medical practice.

All posters are available for download on the federal and state DOL websites.

Appropriate vs. Inappropriate Actions

Some common practices that can be inappropriate in terms of employment revolve around candidate interviews. Knowing the right (and wrong) kinds of questions to ask may seem simple, but in reality, it is quite complex. Questions about the candidate's age, marital status, and place of residence are appropriate for a health physical, but not for an employment interview. The medical practice executive can help supervisors learn how to interview as well as learn what is considered an appropriate action vs. an inappropriate one.

Supervisory Responsibilities

A supervisor is responsible for following the law. Well-meaning intentions to assist an older worker by giving higher-paid work to a younger worker because the older worker might be tired, or not promoting a pregnant worker because she needs her rest while pregnant, will lead to employee grievances for discriminatory practices. If a supervisor is ever unsure of the correct practice, he or she should consult with the medical practice executive, who should be conversant with such laws.

Supervisory Review and Monitoring Functions

Management by expectation is a first step toward compliance, but management by inspection provides a practical way to demonstrate compliance with the law. Observing appropriate human resource practices helps the medical group executive know whether a practice is being followed and the areas for which additional education and training may be needed.

Measuring compliance with the law is another way to determine that all human resource functions are being followed. Auditing personnel records for I-9 forms and completed employment applications and reviewing whether all employees received and signed receipt of the employee handbook are important measures that the medical practice executive can conduct.

Documentation

Memory does not constitute documentation, nor does the statement, "I'm too busy. I don't have time to document." Documentation is the cornerstone of human resource management and the medical practice executive's responsibility, and it is a critical element for any follow-up needed on resolving any issue.

Investigation

Sometimes, the medical practice executive needs to conduct an investigation to gather information that will inform a decision. For example, an employee may have completed the employment application by answering "No" to the question "Have you ever been convicted of a felony?" However, a background check may reveal that the employee has a record with a conviction. The practice executive needs to investigate the accuracy of the data collected and interview the employee for further information prior to making a decision on any new data.

Employee discipline and termination is another supervising function that cannot be overlooked. It is usually the policy of a medical practice to terminate an employee who has falsified information on an employment application.

Maintaining compliance with employment laws is accomplished through continuous review and monitoring of human resource policies, procedures, and practices. By keeping current on practices that affect the medical group, the group executive can align organizational needs with human resource law. Attention to detail and commitment to compliance become part of the management culture and enable the medical group to function appropriately within the confines of the law.

Helpful Resources

The DOL has developed several tools to ensure that America's employers and workers have access to clear and accurate information and assistance. These include:

- eLaws Advisors (www.dol.gov/elaws/advisors.html) are Web-based interactive tools that help small businesses and workers understand most federal employment laws enforced by the DOL.
- The Wage and Hour Division's Website (www.dol.gov/whd/) provides access to a wide range of services and employment and regulatory information. The Wage and Hour Division of the DOL is responsible for enforcing all federal labor laws.
- The EEOC's Website (www.eeoc.gov) has a wealth of information about workplace discrimination laws and regulations.

Your medical practice's legal counsel, industry and small business associations, local employer's council and chamber of commerce, and other practices offer forums for learning about employment laws.

Conclusion

The successful practice administrator plays a pivotal role in the training and development of staff as well as the management of compliance programs related to labor law. The knowledge and skills required to effectively complete this role include development and dissemination of training compliance policies and employee handbooks as well as identifying the training and development needs of staff and implementing appropriate training mechanisms to support those needs.

Notes

1. Adrienne Hill and Rose Wagner, "Growing Pains: Onboarding New Physicians," *MGMA Connexion* 13, no. 2 (2013): 35–36.
2. Tony Fong, "Strong Message: Fletcher Allen Official Received Two-Year Sentence," *Modern Healthcare* (May 2, 2005): 17.
3. Peter Coy, "The Future of Work," *Business Week* (Mar. 22, 2005), 50.
4. Laura Palmer, "Successful Partnerships Yield Better Quality Patient Care," *MGMA Connexion* 14, no. 1 (2014): 21–23.
5. Patrick Lencioni, *The FIVE Dysfunctions of a TEAM* (San Francisco: Jossey-Bass, 2002), 195.
6. "What Is Undue Hardship," Employment FAQ, U.S. Office of Personnel Management (OPM), www.opm.gov/faq/employment/What-is-an-undue-hardship-2.ashx.
7. "Executive Orders: Washington–Obama: Data Table," The American Presidency Project, www.presidency.ucsb.edu/data/orders.php.
8. "Executive Orders: Washington–Obama: Data Table."
9. "Legislation and Policy," Rehabilitation Services Administration, U.S. Department of Education, https://rsa.ed.gov/policy.cfm; "Vocational Rehabilitation and Employment (VR&E)," U.S. Department of Veterans Affairs, modified Dec. 10, 2014, www.benefits.va.gov/vocrehab/index.asp.

Chapter 4

Developing and Implementing Staff Compensation and Benefit Plans

Compensation is the total amount of monetary and nonmonetary pay provided to an employee by an employer in return for work performed as required. Benefits are one component of a total compensation package and are usually indirect or nonmonetary rewards for employment. Some benefits are mandated by law (such as Social Security, unemployment compensation, and workers' compensation) and others vary from employer to employer or industry to industry (such as health insurance, life insurance, medical plan, paid vacation, and pension).

The basic skills required to effectively manage staff compensation and benefits include evaluating insurance, retirement, and other benefits; benchmarking salary data to similar organizations; developing a compensation strategy; and administering compensation and benefit plans.

Basic Compensation

Compensation must be fair, equitable, and related to the job tasks that the person is expected to perform. Employees may initially be paid based on their skill, knowledge, or competency-based expertise. The higher the employee's skill or competency, the higher the pay. For example, a manager with a bachelor's degree is usually paid less than someone with a master's degree. If an incentive program is developed, it should be fair, consistent, and measurable. The criteria should be easily understood and be able to be tracked.

A performance-based compensation model is the most common type of compensation model provided to employees. It is based on merit and is easy to develop, track, and administer. Employees are hired at a salaried or hourly wage and provided wage increases based on how well they performed in a previous period. Incentive pay options allow the employee to receive a bonus based on completing predetermined job goals. If the goals aren't achieved, the employee doesn't receive an increase in pay. For example, a medical group may decide that an average performer receives a 3 percent increase and an exceptional performer receives a 4 percent increase. A determination of the difference between average and high performers is needed for such merit increases.

Physician Compensation

The way a medical practice compensates its physicians for services provided is one of the most important issues affecting a medical group and can ultimately determine the success or failure of the practice. A physician may be paid based on knowledge or skill. A physician with dual-board certification may be paid more than a physician without that certification. A cardiologist may be paid more than a pediatrician, based on the cardiologist's skill, job knowledge, and additional years of training. In addition, a physician may be provided with a fixed salary based on anticipated work with a formula for a bonus or incentive if the workload is exceeded.

Physician compensation will reflect a medical practice's mix of physicians and its legal and cost structure, along with its culture, history, and external influences. Regardless of the plan, the compensation method must reflect the medical practice's goals. It must reward productivity that is consistent with the mission and values of the organization. It must be fair and consistently administered, simple and easily understood, and comply with the law. It should be aligned with the financial needs of the organization and allow the medical group to retain current providers and recruit new providers. Above all, the plan must be fair.[1] For more extensive information about physician compensation, please see Chapter 8 of the *Operations Management* volume in the Body of Knowledge Review series.

Staff Compensation

The medical practice executive should routinely evaluate position compensation based on internal and external factors, evaluating the initial pay offered an employee and the merit increases that an employee receives over time. Adjustments in pay tables and ranges should occur at the same time each year to allow for a consistent process and approach unless there are extenuating circumstances. Pay adjustments should be communicated to employees in writing, including the reason for the adjustment. A poorly run program may allow inconsistencies to enter a system, thus creating unintentional pay inequities.

Developing a Compensation System

Creating the foundation for compensation administration begins by considering the following questions:

- Who will develop and oversee the compensation system?
- Who will provide expert advice?
- What is the budget for developing and maintaining the system?
- When will development occur and how will this ongoing task be carried out?
- Who determines salary ranges and salary increases? How often and on what basis are these done?

It is often helpful to retain a consultant to set up a compensation system and to provide ongoing compensation consulting. Consider using a benefits consulting firm or refer questions to an industry association, such as the Medical Group Management Association (MGMA®), for information and assistance. In any case, it is imperative that the senior management team is involved in establishing the compensation philosophy and policy for the practice. It is also important to set up a compensation committee that represents all the various departments to ensure input across the practice.

The compensation committee should tackle the hard questions about how to establish pay structures for various types of employees. For example, should there be a difference between how clinical and nonclinical staff are compensated? It should also decide how wages or salaries are complemented by benefits and incentives. These three components compose the total compensation package that job candidates consider when making a decision on whether to join your medical practice and that current employees consider when making a decision on whether to stay with the practice.

Developing a compensation system begins with evaluating jobs based on the content of the work, the value of the work to the organization, the culture of the workplace, and external market forces. Compensation begins with job evaluation and moves on to establishing pay, benefits, and incentives.

Job Evaluation

Job evaluation is the first and most important step in compensation administration. Using job descriptions helps determine the relative worth of a job in relation with other jobs in the medical practice. It involves formal comparison of the essential functions of various positions in order to rank each position in the organization. While job content is a primary factor in evaluation, market conditions, competition, worker supply and demand, and unemployment rates are also considered.

Job evaluation is a system procedure designed to aid in establishing pay differentials among jobs with a single employer. It helps you assess:

- A job's relative importance within the organization;
- The knowledge, skills, and abilities necessary to do the job;
- The difficulty level of one job compared to another; and
- The education, experience, and licensing requirements.

Using all of this information, you can develop an equitable and meaningful wage and salary system in line with federal and state laws, which are discussed later in this chapter.

Job Evaluation Methods

There are a number of different job evaluation methods, and the four most popular methods are discussed here. There are advantages and disadvantages for each. In all cases, check your results with industry market data to make sure that your jobs match the market rate for similar jobs, which usually requires using accurate market-pricing surveys.

There is no perfect job evaluation method. You and your medical practice will need to decide which method works best for the type and size of the practice.

Ranking method. The ranking method involves ranking the job descriptions in order from highest to lowest in each department based on a definition of value or contribution. It works best when there are just a few jobs (less than 30) to be evaluated. A matrix is then developed to show the compensation committee how the jobs rank across departments.

The designated human resource professional or a committee can rank jobs department by department. The ranker puts the job titles in order by value. You can also give each job a subjective weight to reflect what the rankers think they are worth. Jobs can be evaluated in pairs by comparing two jobs side by side and then one is chosen as more valuable to the organization than the other. The rankers then develop a chart showing all jobs within each department in order from most valuable to least valuable.

After all jobs are ranked, pay grades are established (entry level/beginner, junior, middle, senior, etc.) for each position in each department. Pay scales are then assigned for each pay grade after checking to see how similar jobs in the community are compensated.

In this competitive compensation analysis process, establishing benchmarks is helpful. A benchmark job is a job common to the industry with easy-to-compare basic characteristics. Benchmark jobs have these characteristics:

- Well-known characteristics that are relatively stable over time;
- Commonalities across employers;
- Components representative of an entire range of jobs; and
- Acceptance in the external marketing for setting wages.

Benchmark jobs (or key jobs) are selected and then compared with what other medical practices are paying their employees in the same job. For example, an X-ray technician position, which has similar functions across medical practices, can be used when validating the average pay in the community. By reviewing the market price of the benchmark jobs within the medical practice industry and your community, your medical practice can establish a pay scale.

Advantages and disadvantages of the ranking method. The advantages of the ranking method are that it is:

- Simple;
- Fast;
- Easy to understand and explain to employees; and
- The least-expensive method.

The disadvantages of the ranking method are that:

- It is based on nonquantitative decisions instead of essential functions, knowledge, skills, and abilities needed for a job;
- There are no standards for comparisons; and
- It is cumbersome when there are many jobs to evaluate.

Job classification method. Classification is similar to the ranking method except that it involves organizing jobs into broad classes or categories based on job analysis findings and building a hierarchy. It uses some comparison standards, such as the complexity of the work and the amount of supervisory responsibility.

The designated human resource professional or a committee groups each job into different classes (typically there are 7 to 14 classes). Many classes allow variability and diversity. Too many classes, however, inhibit their use as common denominators. Each class should be defined, and, like job descriptions, class descriptions are only useful when they represent meaningful similarities and differences among jobs.

After the classes are identified and defined, benchmark jobs are selected as reference points similar to the job ranking method. Classification methods are typically occupation or industry specific. The government, for example, has a Defense Civilian Intelligence Personnel system based on job classifications.

Advantages and disadvantages of job classification. The advantages of the job classification system is that it is:

- Simple;
- Fairly fast; and
- Easy to understand and explain to employees.

The disadvantages of the job classification system are that:

- The standards used are not exact;
- Jobs may be forced into a class that does not quite fit;
- It relies on subjective judgments; and
- It may build biases based on gender, race, and so forth.

Factor comparison method. The factor comparison approach is used to evaluate jobs using two criteria:

1. A set of compensable factors, and
2. Wages for benchmark jobs.

These criteria form a job comparison scale that can be used to set wages for nonbenchmark jobs. This method is complex and not popular.

The designated human resource professional or a committee usually does the factor comparisons. Typically four or five compensable factors are used, such as skills, responsibilities, effort (physical and mental), working conditions, and so forth. For each benchmark job, the hourly wage is then divided up among the identified compensable factors. This produces a rate of pay for each factor for each benchmark job. After benchmark jobs have been factored, all other jobs are compared to the benchmarks and the rates of pay for each factor.

For example, consider an administrative assistant. The hourly wage might be $14 per hour. The committee may value the factors as shown in Exhibit 4.1.

Advantages and disadvantages of factor comparison. The advantages of the factor comparison method are that:

- Value is expressed in dollar amounts;
- It can be easily applied to a variety of jobs;
- It can be easily applied to newly created positions; and
- It adds flexibility.

EXHIBIT 4.1

Factor Comparison

Hourly Wage	Skills	Responsibilities	Effort	Working Conditions
$14.00	$4.00	$3.00	$6.50	$0.50

The disadvantages of the factor comparison method are that it:

- Relies on subjective judgments;
- May build biases based on gender, race, and so forth;
- Is difficult to explain to employees; and
- Is time consuming.

Point factor method. The point factor method looks at a job's specific duties and responsibilities (essential functions) and awards points to each. It is an extension of the factor comparison method. The points are arbitrary, but they reflect the value your medical practice attaches to each function. The practice would assign the highest point value to the essential function it most values, for example, customer service.

As with the factor comparison method, the point factor method uses a set of key factors (e.g., skills, responsibilities, effort, and working conditions). Each of the key factors are then subfactored into levels and then further into prioritized degrees. Points are assigned for each degree and then added up for each degree, level, and key factor to calculate a total point score for each job. Jobs are then grouped together by total score ranges and assigned to a wage or salary grade. Thereby similar jobs are placed in the same wage or salary grade.

Typical key factors and levels are shown in Exhibit 4.2.

Advantages and disadvantages of the point factor method. The advantages of the point factor method are:

- Value is expressed in dollar amounts;
- It can be easily applied to a variety of jobs;
- It can be easily applied to newly created positions; and
- It helps eliminate bias.

EXHIBIT 4.2

Point Factor Method

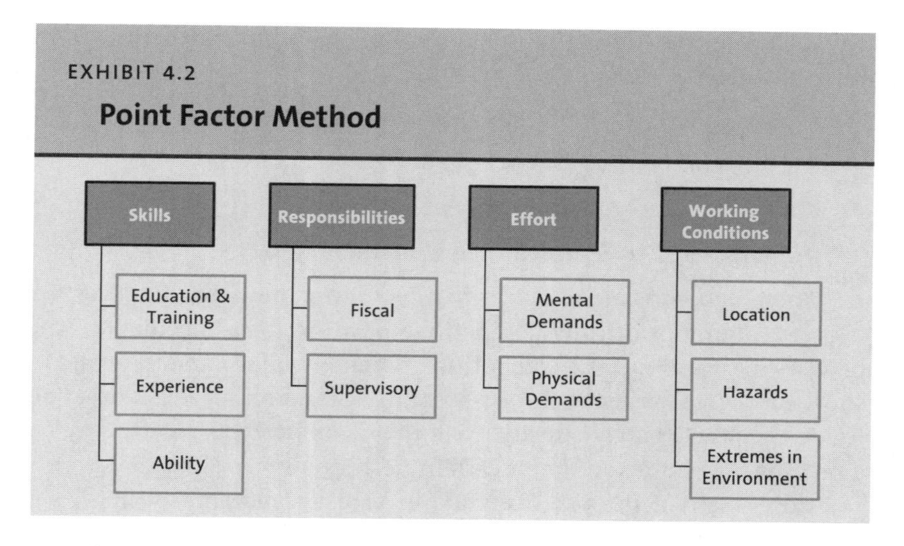

The disadvantages of the point factor method are that:

- It is complex;
- It is time consuming;
- Pay judgments are subjective; and
- It is difficult to explain to employees.

Computing Pay

After each job has been evaluated, the next step is to determine the dollar value that each position is worth. Pay computation involves determining the:

- Number of pay structures needed;
- Number of pay grades within each structure;
- Minimum, midpoint, and maximum pay for each grade;
- Ways individuals can advance in pay grades;
- Record-keeping and reporting requirements; and
- Methods for communicating to employees about compensation.

Your medical practice's compensation committee has to determine where the practice wants to fit in the market in terms of compensation.

For each job, the compensation committee determines where it is on the pay scale:

- Premium (6 to 10 percent above market rates);
- Fully competitive (5 percent above market rates);
- Competitive (equal to market rates); or
- Marginal (1 to 5 percent below market rates).

These decisions are critical when recruiting and retaining staff. By taking a premium or fully competitive position for a specific job, the practice may beat out the competition when qualified candidates are in short supply. However, if this philosophy is used for all jobs and at all times, the practice may quickly reach the salary budget. Usually, paying a premium is justified only for certain positions at certain times.

Conversely, if the practice chooses to use a marginal scale, fewer qualified candidates may be willing to join the practice unless the total compensation package offers something of value to certain candidates. For example, you might offer medical assistants an extremely flexible schedule that appeals to mothers. Typically, using a competitive strategy works best as long as the option of using the other strategies for some positions is available.

Setting the Pay Grades

Your medical practice may decide to have one or more pay structures for different categories of workers, for example, a different one for higher-level administrators. If the practice is a small group, however, a single pay structure is usually adequate.

For a small group, four to five pay grades within its single pay structure work well. For a larger group, there may be as many as 40 within a single pay structure. Regardless of the number of pay grades, keep in mind these tips:

- Cluster positions so that those of the same general value are assigned to the same pay grade;
- Place positions that are different in value in different pay grades; and
- Ensure that the pay grades reasonably conform to pay patterns in your labor market area.

As mentioned earlier, the compensation committee sets the minimum, midpoint, and maximum pay levels for each pay grade. The minimum is typically set at a level that would be acceptable as a starting salary by 80 to 90 percent of the candidates. The midpoint should be high enough to retain employees when they have reached a high level of proficiency. The maximum would be used to retain the most competent employees.

For entry-level jobs, the range between each of the pay levels is small (e.g., 20 to 25 percent); at the higher-level positions, the range is usually broader (e.g., 35 to 40 percent) to ensure the flexibility needed to retain managers and administrators. Your medical practice should use a standard percentage difference (usually 5 to 10 percent) between midpoints for adjoining pay grades to ensure consistency in your pay structure. In healthcare organizations, there often is a small difference for lower-skilled employees, perhaps as low as 3 to 5 percent. At higher skill levels, usually there are higher midpoint differences between pay grades.

The pay range within each pay grade should provide opportunities for employee growth. Spreads typically vary from 10 to 25 percent on either side of the midpoint. Again, higher-level positions will generally have a wider pay grade range. The range spread is typically expressed in a percentage change from the midpoint. For example, the range spread for a pay grade might be plus or minus 10 percent from the midpoint.

Pay grades can have a maximum pay scale so that an employee may hit the top of the range. Organizations need to determine whether the employee is *redlined* and not eligible for any pay increases or whether there is a special incentive program available to senior employees.

Published salary surveys use data from internal and external sources to develop a tool that can be invaluable to a medical group to know the financial factors to consider regarding employee compensation. Such tools include salary groups and pay scales within each salary group. Professional associations, such as MGMA, print benchmarked salary data for physicians and staff. The federal government also publishes national data on certain positions that can help a medical practice determine the kind of pay scale it wants to have for a particular position. These updated data help the medical practice executive determine whether the practice's ranges should be adjusted to reflect changing market rates.

Understanding the Labor Market

The marketplace needs to be considered when developing compensation scales. The marketplace must always be considered in recruiting well-qualified employees and to keep employee turnover low. An unusual economic condition, such as a period of inflation or recession, will also affect the kinds of pay scales offered to employees.

The local market may require a medical practice to take a different approach from national or regional approaches. A medical practice located in a rural or urban area may need to offer a higher rate of pay or other incentives to encourage a person to join the practice. A potential employee needs to see that the higher compensation or benefits are worth the potential change in quality of life.

A practice may need to recruit outside of its local area because of shortages in a certain type of position. A tougher labor market to recruit a particular position will result in a medical group having to pay a higher market rate for that position. For example, a pharmacist shortage may require the medical practice to seek candidates from nearby metropolitan areas or even pursue a national search. These commitments become very expensive recruiting efforts and require additional recruiting support to deal with new issues of travel costs, introduction to the community, costs of a real estate agent, housing relocation expenses, and other transition costs.

Adjust for Time and Other Factors

The medical practice executive should evaluate pay scales periodically to ensure that there is parity within the pay grades. Sometimes a position within the marketplace changes and requires a modification of pay. When new hires are brought into the organization at a higher rate of pay than is traditional, internal parity needs to be made for other comparable positions within the organization to ensure equitable pay.

Job-Driven Compensation

How compensation scales are developed determines how successful the medical group is in attracting and retaining employees. Difficult-to-recruit positions, such as certified coders and nuclear medicine technologists, may have special or higher pay scales. Some positions may require a higher-than-average starting salary to be competitive in the marketplace.

Some positions are difficult to recruit for because of intense external competition. There may be a shortage of qualified candidates for a certain position in the local market because of few if any formal training programs or an increase in need caused by a growing industry. For example, nurses are difficult to recruit because there are so many groups trying to recruit the same labor pool — from hospitals, nursing homes, and home care agencies, to schools, medical groups, and public health agencies. This external competition leads organizations to consider paying nurses at higher rates or deciding to run a practice with staff members who have lower skills levels (e.g., using medical assistants).

Certain positions may even warrant a medical practice to offer a sign-on bonus for difficult-to-fill positions. With shortages in nurses, radiology technologists, professional coders, and other competitive positions, attracting good candidates may require offering retention bonuses given to the employee after staying on the job for a 6- or 12-month period.

Recruitment packages need to be sensitive to the current workforce and current staffing. If coworkers see that tremendous resources are placed on recruiting additional staff but no resources are devoted to retain current employees, there may be perceived inequity issues, which may prompt certain employees to leave the medical practice and thus create a larger recruitment issue for the practice.

Wage compression can also occur wherein all the positions in a like category make similar wages because of the labor market. For example, all professional coders may make a similar wage regardless of experience because most of the coders are being paid toward the top of the compensation range. This compression makes it difficult to manage ongoing resources for other employees who may expect the same type of plan for themselves.

Informal Salary Information Sources

Informal salary surveys allow the organization to respond to changing market forces. During the recruitment process, human resource professionals glean large amounts of information from candidates, including salary and benefits data. If potential candidates will not work for a medical group because of "low pay," as indicated on the survey, this kind of information should be revealed during the interview process. Also, new hires may validate the competitive pay and benefits of the employer when they sign up for their benefits in the new organization. Data from these types of encounters can be invaluable for the organization.

In addition, peers can share data about why employees are leaving a certain organization, and exit interviews can provide other anecdotal information about an employee's personal experience. For example, an employee may share that he is leaving the medical group to work at a competitor's organization in the same job for a one-dollar-an-hour increase in pay. However, all the factors would need to be considered. In this case, at the competitor's office, the employee would receive an additional $2,080 in annual salary ($1 × 2,080 full-time hours worked per year), but would also have to pay $3,000 out of pocket for benefits. The net effect would be a salary loss of $920 because of increased benefits costs. This result suggests that the employee might have additional or unstated reasons for leaving the organization.

Confidentiality of Compensation Data

The medical group needs to determine what types of compensation or pay information can be shared with employees and what information should remain private. For example, a group may elect to keep salaries private, but communicate the bonus structure with everyone, telling staff and physicians that is calculated based on seniority, pay grade, or other factors. Private information is, obviously, private and confidential. It should not be shared with other people and should remain protected information in the employee file.

A medical practice should have a policy on what type of pay information is shared. A closed policy is one that does not openly share pay grades or ranges. For example, a position is posted and the pay grade is 23, which means that the position's minimum pay is $12 per hour and maximum pay is $16 per hour. This open policy allows employees to know whether they are interested in this position or not.

A closed policy would not post a pay grade, may not openly share that information, and would share pay information only to a final candidate being considered. Knowing whether to share certain kinds of pay information helps the medical practice executive to focus on following its policies.

Sharing such data can create conflict and tension. However, certain groups, such as government agencies, share salary information openly, and this is a common expectation for this group. Overall, salary information should be kept confidential and staff should be encouraged to maintain confidentiality regarding salaries.

Formal Benefits

Whereas an employee's direct pay is easily seen, the indirect pay, consisting of the employee's benefits, retirement benefits, and Social Security, is often overlooked. Formal benefits may include medical, dental, and vision plans, short- and long-term disability insurance, life insurance, pension plan, savings and investment plans, unemployment insurance, and workers' compensation premiums, among others. These benefits usually have a shared cost between the employer and employee based on a certain percentage. In larger organizations, the pay–benefit mix in total compensation could be 20 percent of the employee's wages. For example, an employee making $30,000 per year could expect to receive approximately $6,000 in additional benefits from the organization.

A flexible benefit plan allows employees to choose from a range of benefits that best meet their current needs. There may be a dollar-amount cap to apply to those benefits. For example, one employee may have a $1,500 cap that is applied to a $1,000 medical premium and a $500 vision premium, and another employee may apply her $1,500 to a $750 dental premium and $750 toward a medical premium.

Benchmarking data helps the employer determine whether the benefit package being offered to employees is competitive within the marketplace. If the market shows that employers generally provide benefits up to 20 percent of the employee payroll and a particular employer provides only 10 percent, that factor may influence whether an employee will join the organization.

Benefits have short- and long-term effects on the employee base. A practice may decide to fund a certain benefit today but regret its financial effect on the group in the future. As an example, in the past, the automobile industry decided to fully fund retiree health premiums when costs were well within control and there were few retirees. However, with an aging workforce and retirees living longer, the financial impact has become cost prohibitive, prompting the industry to decide how to handle benefits for the future. These lessons learned can help medical groups design benefit packages that are fair, equitable, and affordable for both the employee and employer.

Goal-Driven Benefits

The size and/or type of a group practice may preclude it from offering standard benefits that compete on equal footing with those of other groups. If this is the case at your practice, consider focusing on goal-based benefits to attract new employees and motivate existing ones.

Equity ownership. Equity ownership may allow a physician to participate in owning a part of the medical practice, which would allow the physician to participate in any financial gains. In for-profit organizations that allow stock to be purchased, an employee can purchase stock in the company and have equity ownership. On the downside, equity ownership also means sharing losses.

Some medical groups have shareholders and nonshareholders. Compensation methods will be different for the two groups. For example, depending on the legal structure, a physician may have stock options or direct ownership in a medical group. This arrangement will affect how the physician is paid.

Profit sharing. A medical group may decide to offer its employees the opportunity to participate in a profit-sharing program that provides employees with additional pay if the medical group meets or exceeds its financial goals. The challenge is to decide how much of the profit will be distributed and to whom. Or, bonuses may be provided if the practice meets its financial goals.

As an incentive to achieve department goals, a medical practice may decide to provide a team reward if the team achieves a certain financial outcome. For example, a medical group with an urgent care center may provide an incentive for the team who sees more than 50 patients a day. This goal would mean the team would be required to get all the patients through the center on a timely basis and avoid any walk-outs from the clinic caused by patients waiting too long.

Gainsharing. Gainsharing is a process by which employees are involved in performance enhancements and share the financial benefits of these improvements made by the medical practice. Gainsharing is a common practice among Fortune 500 companies. Unlike bonuses that are provided annually, gainsharing allows regular financial payments to be made to the employee, such as on a monthly or quarterly basis. The system instills immediate understanding by the employee on what needs to be accomplished to achieve a gainsharing bonus. Although the system may be incomplete on providing incentives to employees to achieve all organizational goals, this tool has been used for many companies to achieve phenomenal results.

Insurance Benefits

The types of insurance that may be offered are generally health and/or life.

Health insurance. With more than 42 million people in the United States currently lacking health insurance,[2] and many Americans believing healthcare is a basic right, access to health insurance coverage is a key benefit for a medical practice. Employees may seek employment based on whether the employer offers health insurance. While it might be the case that some smaller medical practices do not offer health insurance to their employees, most larger practices have to offer health insurance to competitively recruit employees.

Some medical groups contract with external groups to handle their health insurance coverage. Other medical practices may cover their own health insurance through a self-insured plan. Regardless of the arrangement, health insurance must be managed effectively and efficiently, with cost containment being one of the largest issues plaguing medical practices today.

In addition to basic health insurance, additional specific health-related insurance may include the following:

- **Dental, vision, and hearing insurance.** Dental and/or vision insurance offerings can be employer and/or employee funded and offer coverage under health maintenance organization, preferred provider organization, or traditional plans. Hearing and vision insurance may be options for employees and/or their dependents who experience hearing and/or vision problems.
- **In-house medical services.** As an employee benefit, medical practices may offer access to certain types of medical services within the organization. Services may range from free access for physician services to reduced fees for pharmaceuticals and medical supplies.
- **Long-term and short-term disability insurance.** Short-term disability coverage defines plan days covered, plan funding, and what is and is not considered a short-term disability. Plans that allow pregnancy as a short-term disability are very popular for employers with a potentially child-bearing workforce.

Postemployment medical benefits. The Health Insurance Portability and Accountability Act of 1996 (HIPAA) was approved to amend the Internal Revenue Code (IRC) of 1986. Its primary purpose is to improve portability and continuity of health insurance coverage, eliminate misuse in health insurance and its delivery, promote medical savings account use, improve access to long-term-care services, and simplify health insurance administration.

Consolidated Omnibus Budget Reconciliation Act of 1985. Access to medical benefits through the Consolidated Omnibus Budget Reconciliation Act (COBRA) is offered for up to 18 months after an employee leaves an organization; postretirement medical benefits are offered only to those employees who officially retire. Qualified retirees may need to meet certain age requirements, and payment of medical benefits may be based on years of service at the organization prior to retiring.

COBRA amends the Employee Retirement Income Security Act of 1974 (ERISA), the IRC, and the Public Health Service Act of 1944 to ensure the continuation of group health coverage that otherwise would have been terminated. And HIPAA provides additional detail to COBRA.

COBRA allows certain former employees and dependents to temporarily continue health coverage at group rates, which are usually less expensive than private health coverage. In general, the law applies to health plans with 20 or more employees and requires that the plan have rules detailing how an individual becomes entitled to these benefits. Life insurance is not covered under COBRA.

Long-term care plans. As the population continues to age, long-term care plans are becoming more popular. For an employee–employer contribution, the plan covers the cost for a certain percentage of care provided in an approved long-term-care facility.

Life Insurance. Life insurance may be just for the employee, or the practice may offer a plan for the employee and dependents. The plan will have limits usually based on the employee's income or a percentage of his or her income. In addition to life insurance policies that cover general death benefits, some employers offer coverage for accidental death, such as caused by automobile or plane crashes.

Retirement and Severance Benefits

Employer contributions to retirement plans allow the employee to have money available for retirement. The plan may be fully funded by the employer or may have joint employer and employee contributions.

Severance pay. As more organizations are downsizing; going bankrupt; or going through mergers, acquisitions, and consolidations; they have developed a severance pay policy for employees whose positions are eliminated. Usually, these policies are based on the employee's employment status (full- vs. part-time), class (exempt vs. nonexempt, management vs. executive), and years of service (less than one year, one to five years, five or more years). These differentiations will determine the level of severance provided to an employee.

Issues Related to Benefits

The costs of benefits add up, especially as a practice grows, and pose legal implications. Be sure you understand what effect a benefit will have on the practice before offering it.

Benefit cost sharing. Employers determine which benefits are employer paid, which are employee paid, and which are shared by both the employer and employee. Inflation, malpractice premium increases, and reduced reimbursement from managed care plans, among other factors, affect the bottom line of many practices. Therefore, employees pick up more of the cost of benefits. The employer must be careful with this strategy, however, because it may lead to higher turnover and a medical practice that is less effective in the marketplace. Although this shift in payment responsibility may be a cost-effective approach for the employer, it may strap the employee with higher costs and a perceived drop in quality of life, leading to employee dissatisfaction.

A medical practice may choose to be self-funding for a certain part of its benefit costs. For example, it may contract out its life insurance and short-term disability benefits but self-fund its health insurance costs through its own insurance plan or medical malpractice through an offshore captive insurance company.

Eligibility. Benefit plans can be established for certain employee types and classes of employees. A medical practice can define the difference between full-time and part-time employment for benefit purposes. A full-time position may be 36 hours or more of work per week, which allows the employee to participate in the full-time benefit plan, whereas part-time benefits would be available for employees working from 20 to 35 hours a week. Those employees who work fewer than 20 hours each week could be considered ineligible for benefits. More benefits would be available for the full-time employee as an incentive to work full time. Examples would be that a full-time employee would receive reduced premiums on health insurance and an employer-paid short-term disability benefit, whereas a part-time employee would receive a higher medical premium and no short-term disability benefit.

Benefits could also vary based on job class so that a physician receives a different type of benefit structure than a nonphysician staff member. The benefit package, however, needs to be carefully designed with appropriate human resource office and legal counsel input to ensure that the plan meets federal and state legal requirements and doesn't violate any specific laws. For example, the medical practice may want to offer a pension plan to physicians and nonphysician employees but offer a shorter vesting period for physicians. That change in benefit may not be allowed based on how the practice and employees are organized. Legal counsel can review pension laws to determine what kinds of variables are allowed.

Legal and Tax Issues Related to Retirement Plans

Retirement plans can be qualified or nonqualified. Qualified plans do not discriminate among employees, are tax exempt, and offer a tax deferral benefit for employee and employer contributions. Qualified plans allow the medical practice a tax deduction for plan contributions wherein employees do not pay taxes on plan assets until they are distributed, and plan earnings are tax deferred. To maintain a qualified status, an employer must follow the requirements of the Internal Revenue Service (IRS), the Department of Labor (DOL), and ERISA.

A nonqualified plan has easy plan adoption and no coverage, eligibility, or participation requirements. It allows contributions beyond caps established for qualified plans. A medical practice can decide to provide nonqualified deferred compensation plans to only a select group of employees (e.g., physicians). Whereas a qualified plan must be written and must meet participation, vesting, and funding requirements, a nonqualified plan need not meet these requirements. A nonqualified plan allows the employee to get more compensation.

However, nonqualified plans have drawbacks. The medical practice won't claim a tax deduction for employee amounts until the employee receives that money as income, perhaps many years in the future. The employee may not receive the money at all, however, if the medical practice becomes insolvent, because that money is subject to the claims of the medical practice's creditors; in other words, it is unsecured.

Some benefits are legally required, such as payment of unemployment benefits, workers' compensation premiums, and holding funds for federal, state, and local taxes. When designing a compensation and benefits program, the medical practice must be aware of the applicable laws and how they may affect the development of the plan.

Employee Retirement Income Security Act. For the medical practice, ERISA is a federal law that sets minimum standards for voluntary established pension and health plans to protect plan participants. ERISA requires participants to be provided with information such as plan features and funding, participation standards, vesting, benefit accrual and funding, fiduciary responsibilities for assets, and a grievance and appeals process.

Medical Practice Payroll Obligations

Every medical practice, as an employer, must report to the IRS with regard to the income paid to each employee. The medical practice should determine the amount of income tax to withhold. The medical practice, based on its size, will either deposit the taxes it withholds for future payment to the IRS or will send it directly to the IRS. The three components of federal payroll taxes are federal income taxes withheld from the employee's wages, the employees' share of Federal Insurance Contributions Act of 1935 (FICA) taxes, and the employer's matching share of FICA taxes.

FICA comprises a Medicare hospital insurance tax of 1.45 percent on all taxable wages and Old-Age, Survivors, and Disability Insurance (OASDI) of 6.2 percent (commonly called *Social Security*). Therefore, a medical practice must withhold 7.65 percent of each employee's wage and match this amount with its own funds.

In addition to these taxes, the medical practice may be liable to pay IRC Section 457 plans, workers' compensation insurance, and/or unemployment insurance.

Social Security

The Social Security Act is the law governing most operations of the Social Security program. The original Social Security Act was enacted in 1935 and subsequent amendments comprise 28 titles.[3] The OASDI program is authorized by Title II of the Social Security Act. Social Security is usually referred to as a tax. It is actually the amount of contribution based on a percentage of earnings, up to an annual maximum, that must be paid by employers and employees on wages from employment under FICA. Usually, medical practices withhold contributions from wages, add an equal amount of contributions, and pay both on a current basis.

Internal Revenue Code Section 457 (Deferred Compensation)

IRC Section 457 plans are nonqualified, deferred compensation plans established by state or local government and tax-exempt employers. If a medical practice is considered to be a tax-exempt employer, it would qualify to provide this type of plan. The practice could establish either eligible or ineligible plans, which are subject to the specific requirements and deferral limitations of IRC Section 457.

Workers' Compensation

The concept of workers' compensation (generally known as *workers' comp*) dates back more than 100 years, to 1908, when it was enacted for federal employees. It relates to the liability of the employer to pay damages for employee injuries incurred while the employee is on the job. Workers' compensation includes an elective schedule of compensation and provides a procedure to determine liability and compensation. It is actually an insurance program that pays an employee for medical and disability benefits for work-related injuries or certain diseases.

If an employee is injured on the job, the employee's medical treatment costs are paid by the workers' compensation policy. If the employee has a job-related injury that prevents him or her from working, the employee will receive weekly income through the policy until able to return to work. Medical practices must either obtain coverage by purchasing a workers' compensation insurance policy or become licensed to *self-insure* by the state labor commissioner.

Unemployment Insurance

Unemployment compensation was created by the Social Security Act of 1935 to help eligible people who, through no fault of their own, are unemployed. Monetary benefits are usually determined according to the amount of former wages and/or weeks of work. The program is funded by employer taxes, either federal or state, and is a partnership between the federal and state governments wherein the program is based on federal law but administered by state employees under state law. Each state creates its own program within the guidelines of the federal government. The state statute develops the eligibility and disqualification provisions, benefit amount, state tax base, and state rate.

Miscellaneous Benefits

Recruiting Bonuses

Employees may be provided with a *recruitment, signing,* or *referral* bonus if a person is referred to the medical practice, accepts the position, and stays in the position for a certain period of time. This bonus generates employee buy-in of the recruitment process, creates awareness of difficult-to-recruit positions, and encourages employees to network with others to promote the organization for future employment.

Paid Time Off

An employee may be afforded time off if it does not conflict with the needs of the department and is preapproved by a supervisor. Some employers are moving to a flexible program of paid time off (PTO) that combines time off for sick leave, vacation, holidays, and jury duty into one pool. In this way, the employee manages one "bucket" of time instead of different buckets of time. The PTO plan mitigates situations in which employees would dip into an unrelated bucket, such as an employee who wants a day off and pretends to call in sick because there is no time left in the employee's vacation time bucket but there is time left in the bucket of sick days.

Financial Planning or Counseling

While medical practices may provide retirement resources for the employee through Social Security and a pension plan, those resources may not be enough for the employee at the time of retirement to maintain a certain quality of life. As a result, a voluntary investment plan such as a 401(k) plan would allow the employee to defer receiving compensation in order to have the amount contributed to the plan for future use at retirement. Information on employee assistance programs, including financial counseling, can be found in Chapter 2 of this volume.

Housing Finance Assistance

Owning a house is an integral part of the American dream, and organizations can help employees achieve that dream through offering housing finance assistance. An employee can benefit from housing finance assistance, including financial planning, exploration of options available, and reduced rates through group consortiums.

Child or Elder Care

Caring for family members, such as children or elderly parents, is an important employee value. A medical practice that helps employees address these issues provides a valuable benefit. A medical practice may choose to offer a plan for the employee to save money pretax to pay for these services or may actually offer these services through the practice at a reduced employee rate.

Charitable Matching Contributions

Some medical practices offer a charitable matching program that matches a certain percentage of funds that an employee contributes to a charity. For example, if an employee contributes $100 to the American Red Cross, the employer might contribute 50 percent of the employee's contribution, or $50, to that agency, too. Certain limitations may apply to this benefit, such as contribution caps and eligible charities.

Individual Retirement Accounts

An individual retirement account (IRA) allows an employee to invest pretax dollars in an investment plan that is managed by the employee. It is a self-directed, employee-funded retirement plan. Employers may choose to contribute money to this type of plan instead of managing their own pension plan.

Retirement Planning

Much has been written about the generational diversity in today's workforce, particularly contrasting the baby boomer generation and Generation X. Unfortunately, neither group is saving at a sufficient rate to provide for its retirement.

A qualified retirement plan benefits medical practice owners and employees by providing a mechanism for accumulating retirement savings. It also provides significant tax benefits to the practice and its employees, which is a competitive advantage to the practice for attracting and retaining good employees.

Physician Retirement Savings and Wealth Accumulation

According to Thomas J. Stanley, PhD, and William D. Danko, PhD, authors of *The Millionaire Next Door*, physicians have a low propensity to accumulate substantial personal wealth compared to individuals in other high-earning occupations. The authors attribute this problem, in part, to physicians' late start beginning their practices after many years of education and professional training. The substantial debt obtained to finance this education also hinders a physician's ability to save. Finally, because physicians typically spend long hours taking care of their patients' physical health, they often have little time to devote to managing their own financial health.[4] Because retirement plan assets often comprise a significant portion of a physician's personal savings, selecting and managing these plans is crucial, not just to the medical practice but also as a part of the physician-owners' overall financial plan.

Tax Advantages

The first tax benefit offered by qualified retirement plans and simplified employee pension (SEP) plans is that contributions to the plans are fully tax deductible when made in accordance with tax laws. This means that neither the practice (its owners, in the case of a pass-through entity) nor its employees pay current income taxes on the employer contributions. Second, if an employer permits employee deferrals under a 401(k) arrangement, those contributions are not currently subject to income taxes, although these amounts are subject to applicable Medicare and Social Security taxes for both the employee and the employer.

Another important tax benefit, especially for plan participants, is that the earnings on qualified retirement plan contributions are not subject to income taxes until they are withdrawn. This allows plan assets to grow and compound at a significantly faster rate than investments in a taxable account.

As discussed later in this chapter, distributions from the plan are generally subject to income taxes. But if funds have accumulated in the plan for many years, the absence of income taxes increases the potential for wealth accumulation for the physician-owners and their long-term employees. As discussed earlier, an overlooked but extremely important aspect of retirement plans is the inability to access the funds until retirement. This results in a forced savings program for the physician and typically allows them to retire with a comfortable standard of living.

Importance of Management and Compliance

Qualified retirement plans are subject to a number of federal laws and regulations promulgated by both the DOL and IRS, and penalties for noncompliance can be significant. The trustees and employer sponsor of a plan must ensure proper handling of internal administrative matters, such as remitting deferrals and employer funding on a timely basis. These administrative functions are often delegated to the practice administrator to oversee. The assistance of an outside third-party administrator is an excellent resource to the practice administrator in this role.

Because the plan's financial assets, which are often significant, are important to the retirement security of the practice's employees and physician-owners, the trustees of the plan (often the physicians) should exercise due diligence to ensure that the plan assets are effectively managed. The DOL requires that plan assets be diversified and prudently managed to minimize the potential for large losses.[5] Using third-party vendors to assist in the investment selection, ongoing communication, and staff education achieves this diversification.

An administrator should develop the knowledge and skills necessary to facilitate selection of the practice's qualified retirement plan and its administration and regulatory compliance. This chapter provides a basic overview of some of the significant issues common to a medical practice's qualified retirement plan.

Types of Retirement Plans

Practices will ordinarily choose from several popular options in retirement plans. Because practices usually rely on one or more outside advisors in connection with selecting, maintaining, and administering a plan, the practice administrator does not generally need to be aware of all the technical aspects of the plan. A general knowledge of the various options is sufficient to assist the administrator in assuring physicians and other leaders that the group has considered the available plan designs.

Defined Benefit Plans

A defined benefit plan is one in which the employer contributes an amount necessary to ensure a fixed level of benefits to the employees when they retire. These plans are more complex than defined contribution plans. They require the services of an enrolled actuary to compute the required contribution. Contributions to these plans are mandatory, so if a practice fails to meet the minimum funding standards, it can be subject to excise taxes. Furthermore, the practice may need to purchase insurance coverage to guarantee the benefits from the Pension Benefit Guaranty Corporation.[6]

The use of defined benefit plans by employers has decreased significantly over the past few decades. In 1983, 60 percent of households with a pension were covered by a defined benefit plan. This percentage dropped to 37 percent in 2006.[7] These plans are rarely found in the healthcare industry.

More recently, defined benefit plans have received increased attention from small employers. This is because, at least in part, aging baby boomers realize that they have not saved enough for retirement and are skeptical about the solvency of the Social Security system.[8] Because defined benefit plans allow larger contributions for older employees, they may be appropriate for practices with older physicians who want to put away more money for retirement than the limitation imposed on defined contribution plans.[9] These plans might be prohibitively expensive for practices with a large number of older rank-and-file employees.

Defined Contribution Plans

Benefits available under a defined contribution plan are based on the contributions made to the plan by the employer, the employee, and the associated earnings on these contributions. An individual account is maintained for each participant, and that participant's benefit is based on the amount contributed to their account, plus any income, expenses, gains, losses, or forfeitures from other participants that are allocated to that account. This type of plan is relatively simple to administer and occurs often in medical practices.

Popular types of defined contribution plans include money purchase pension plans, profit-sharing plans (including 401(k) deferral features, integration or cross-tested), and 403(b) plans.

Money Purchase Pension Plans

A money purchase pension plan is a defined contribution plan in which the contributions are calculated in accordance with a formula, but the benefits are not guaranteed. Although these plans were once prevalent in medical practices, they have become less common because the annual funding is mandatory by the employer and, as a result, they offer less flexibility.

Profit-Sharing Plans

A profit-sharing plan often offers the most flexibility of all qualified retirement plans. The practice can elect to contribute as much as 25 percent of the annual covered compensation of all eligible employees. The maximum contribution on behalf of each employee and the amount of annual compensation considered for funding requirements increases periodically based on cost-of-living indexes. Although the employer is not required to make a contribution in any particular year, the IRS does require that contributions be more than sporadic. Revenue Ruling 80-146 states that if a profit-sharing plan receives no contributions for five consecutive years, the IRS will consider that plan to be terminated.[10] These plans are popular with medical practices.

401(k) Plans

Although frequently referred to as "plans" by many, including the media and even the IRS, 401(k) actually refers to an IRC section that describes a feature that can be added to either a profit-sharing or stock bonus plan. A 401(k) deferral allows participants to defer part of their pretax wages into the retirement plan. The plan might also include a provision in which the employer makes a matching contribution based on the employee's deferrals. The matching contribution is the only contingent benefit an employer may use to entice an employee to make elective deferrals to the 401(k) plan. Most businesses, including corporations, partnerships, sole proprietorships, limited liability entities, and non-governmental tax-exempt organizations, may establish a 401(k) plan.[11]

Adding the 401(k) feature to a profit-sharing plan is popular with medical practices. Subject to the provisions discussed later in this chapter, this plan design allows for significant contributions for the physician-owners. It also provides employees with the ability to provide for their own retirement, but often at a lower cost to the practice than other types of plans. Special catch-up deferral provisions are also available to plan participants who have attained at least age 50 during the plan year.

Safe Harbor 401(k) Plans

The basic principle of a safe harbor 401(k) plan is that the employer provides a certain minimum contribution in exchange for being able to eliminate deferral and matching nondiscrimination testing (discussed later in this chapter). The benefit of eliminating this testing is that employees with higher salaries can defer up to the annual limit (adjusted each year) without concern for what other employees defer.

Plan sponsors may choose between two types of contributions: a safe harbor nonelective contribution or a safe harbor matching contribution. These contributions must be 100 percent vested and are not available for hardship or other in-service withdrawals before age 59½. No minimum hours of service can be required and a participant cannot be required to be employed on the last day of the plan year. The nonelective contribution requires the employer to contribute 3 percent of each eligible employee's compensation for the year. The matching contribution requires the employer to match elective deferrals at the rate of 100 percent for the first 3 percent of compensation deferred, plus 50 percent of the next 2 percent deferred.

Plans that meet the safe harbor requirements are generally exempt from the top-heavy rules (discussed later in this chapter).

Newer legislation allows plan sponsors to add a Roth provision to their 401(k) plan. This allows participants to make after-tax contributions to a plan. Subject to some special rules, this makes the future distributions of these contributions and their earnings tax free.

Section 403(b) Plans

Also referred to as tax-sheltered annuities, Section 403(b) plans are retirement plans for employees of tax-exempt organizations, public schools, and cooperative hospital service organizations, as well as certain ministers. Physicians and other employees of universities and hospital systems might be eligible to participate in these plans. Like the 401(k) feature, these plans provide for elective deferrals under a salary reduction arrangement.[12]

Other Plans

Other plan options available include the SEP and cash balance plans.

Simplified employee pension plans. A SEP plan is a not a qualified retirement plan; it is a type of IRA that is funded by the employer. It may receive annual contributions similar to those for money purchase pension and profit-sharing plans.

The fact that these plans have fewer administrative requirements appeals to smaller practices. A major disadvantage, however, is that they do not receive protection from creditor claims because they are not qualified retirement plans.[13] Another disadvantage is that the funding immediately vests with employees and they may withdraw the funds at any time after they are placed into the account. This often results in adverse tax consequences to employees and negatively affects their financial future.

Cash balance plans. Although a cash balance plan is technically a defined benefit plan, it performs like a hybrid arrangement with attributes of both a defined benefit and a defined contribution plan. One advantage to this arrangement is that it can provide for tax-deductible contributions in excess of the defined contribution limitations and can be designed to provide better parity in the level of benefits paid to older and younger workers than a traditional defined benefit plan.[14]

An advanced technique often used by physicians who want to increase funding levels or to catch up on their funding shortfalls from prior years is to combine 401(k) profit-sharing and cash balance plans to achieve their objectives. Like defined benefit plans, cash balance plans require actuarial services and are therefore more expensive to administer than other defined contribution plans.

Setting Up the Plan

Once a practice has determined what type of plan best suits its needs, it must design the plan.

Prototype vs. Individually Designed Plans

First, a practice must decide whether to adopt a prototype plan or to create a plan designed specifically for the practice. Many investment vendors offer prototype plans, which are inexpensive off-the-shelf plan documents, to their clients. One potential disadvantage is that these plans may have limited design flexibility. For example, the practice is usually required to invest its plan assets with the plan's vendor, thus limiting investment flexibility.

Alternatively, a practice may have a professional, often an attorney, draft a plan specifically designed for its practice. Although individually designed plans are flexible, they are usually more expensive to adopt and maintain, especially if future amendments are necessary.

Two key considerations are: (1) the expertise of the vendor providing the document, and (2) the operational and procedural components of the document. The plan document controls all aspects of the plan and should be reviewed by a professional familiar with qualified retirement plans.

Trustees and Fiduciaries

A trustee has a fiduciary responsibility to ensure that the retirement plan operates to secure the plan assets and to pay benefits and plan expenses for the sole benefit of the participants and beneficiaries. As fiduciaries, they have discretionary authority or control over the plan's operations, administration, and investments in accordance with the provisions of the plan document. Trustees must ensure that the plan complies with all regulations of the DOL and IRS.

The trustees may be officers of the group appointed by the board of directors or a professional trustee service offered by a third party. Although the trustees, such as officers of the practice, have the legal responsibility for plan operations, they typically use the services of outside advisors, including third-party administrators, employee benefit firms, accounting firms, and investment advisors.

If a third party exercises discretionary powers over the plan investments, such as in the case of a registered investment advisor, that party may also be considered a fiduciary. Although attorneys, accountants, actuaries, insurance agents, and consultants frequently provide services in connection with a retirement plan, they are not considered fiduciaries unless they exercise discretionary authority over the plan or its assets.[15]

Plan Investments

The practice must make decisions on how it will handle plan investments. One decision is whether to have a self-directed plan, in which participants in defined contribution plans make their own investment decisions regarding their plan assets, or a trustee-directed plan, in which investment decisions are made by the trustees of the plan.

As previously discussed, the trustees have a fiduciary responsibility for investment of the plan's assets. One advantage of self-directed plans is that they offer more flexibility for the individual participants, who may have different investment needs, philosophies, or horizons. A second advantage is that, if this arrangement meets certain DOL criteria defined in ERISA Section 404(c), the trustees have some protection from fiduciary responsibility for the participants' investment decisions.[16]

A major disadvantage to self-directed plans is that they are usually more expensive and more cumbersome to administer. Second, some of the participants may not be knowledgeable regarding investments and require some basic investment education. The practice should exercise caution in providing this information, because doing so can subject the practice, the trustees, and other fiduciaries to legal risk; that is, providing investment information could be construed as giving investment advice. ERISA does provide some safe harbors regarding the provision of investment information, such as use of advice created with a computer model and advice given under an arrangement in which the provider's fees cannot vary based on the investment option selected. The safe harbor includes many additional requirements, such as giving notice and an annual audit by an independent auditor.[17] Because of the risks involved in providing this information, a practice should use due diligence in offering investment information to its participants. This includes having a formal contract with a provider who is knowledgeable in both investments and ERISA requirements.[18] It is often inadvisable for an employer to provide advice to employees regarding their retirement plan investments.

Selective Plan Considerations

Loans to Participants

Some plans allow loans to participants. These loans must carry a reasonable rate of interest, be sufficiently secured, and be granted on a nondiscriminatory basis. The participants must repay the loans under a reasonable repayment schedule, including payments made at least quarterly, with level amortization. (Handling repayment through authorized payroll deductions often works well.) The repayment period of a loan cannot exceed five years, except when the loan relates to the acquisition of the participant's personal residence.

Finally, a participant cannot borrow more than the lesser of $50,000 or 50 percent of the participant's vested balance; otherwise, the proceeds will be treated as a distribution.[19]

The obvious advantage to allowing participant loans is that it provides a mechanism for participants to access their retirement funds to meet an emergency or other financial need. In some instances, employees who cannot borrow from a plan may terminate their employment in order to receive a distribution.

Two disadvantages are that administering participant loans adds time and complexity to managing the plan, and that by taking loans against their balance, employees potentially reduce the amount of funds available for their retirement.

Top-Heavy Considerations

When a plan fails DOL- and IRS-mandated nondiscrimination testing, it may be classified as *top heavy*. A defined contribution plan is generally considered top heavy if, as of the determination date, 60 percent or more of the aggregate account balances accrue to key employees. For a SEP plan, this determination may be based on either aggregate account balances or aggregate contributions.[20]

Medical practice plans are likely to be considered top heavy. If so, regulations require certain minimum benefits and vesting requirements in the plan. If the plan is not top heavy, then normal vesting and funding requirements apply. Most 401(k) plans in smaller medical practices are almost always established using the safe harbor provisions described previously to eliminate any potential refunding of physician-owner deferrals.

Eligibility and Vesting

A qualified plan may have certain age and service limitations as a condition for participation in the plan, except that plans cannot generally exclude employees over the age of 21 who have completed at least one year of service. Special rules may apply for employees who work less than a full-time schedule and those with breaks in service. Once an employee becomes eligible, he or she must begin participating no later than the earlier of the next plan entry date or six months after the date the employee meets eligibility requirements. To satisfy this condition, plans often have two plan entry dates per year — one on the first day of the plan year and one six months later.

Once an employee begins participating, the plan's vesting provisions determine what percentage of an employee's balance is nonforfeitable (e.g., if the employee terminates employment). An employee's own contributions, such as 401(k) deferrals, are never subject to vesting. Funding to the plan under the safe harbor provisions is also not subject to vesting. The law generally allows for vesting of other employer contributions over a three- to seven-year period, with certain minimum amounts vested at the end of each year.

One notable exception to the eligibility and vesting rules is that a plan may require an employee to have two years of service to be eligible to participate in the plan. In this situation the plan must immediately provide 100 percent vesting. The two-years-of-service option is only available for the employer contributions; the plan must still allow for employee contributions after one year. This two-year eligibility and immediate vesting option may be beneficial for practices that have high turnover rates for recently hired employees.[21]

Contribution Formula

Defined contribution plans need to specify how contributions are determined and allocated. This formula must follow certain rules regarding maximum contribution amounts and generally not discriminate in favor of employees with high salaries.

For money purchase pension plans, this formula is especially crucial because it results in a mandatory contribution to the plan each year. If the practice sets this percentage too high, it could create cash flow problems or result in lower physician salaries. If the practice sets this percentage too low, the physicians and employees would have less accumulation in their retirement funds.

Defined contribution plans are generally designed to maximize the contribution of the physicians-owners and balance that with the desired funding level for the staff. This design typically includes a 401(k) deferral option, an employer match, a nonelective contribution that satisfies the safe harbor provisions, and a discretionary profit-sharing contribution (designed to maximize physician-owner contributions). Notice requirements (discussed later in this chapter) allow the practice to satisfy the nondiscrimination testing.[22]

Although qualified plans may not generally discriminate in favor of highly compensated employees, both defined benefit and defined contribution plans may coordinate the plan contribution–benefit formula with payments the practice makes into the Social Security retirement system. This has the effect of reducing the contribution or benefit for the compensation an employee receives that is below the Social Security taxable wage base. These plans are typically referred to as integrated plans, which means integrated with the Social Security wage base.[23] Another popular design is referred to as a *cross-tested plan,* which is based, in part, on the ages of the plan participants. The complexities of this plan design are beyond the scope of this text but are worthy of consideration as part of a practice's plan design.

Because actuaries determine the contribution for traditional defined benefit plans, practices do not generally need to devise a formula for these contributions. The practice does, however, need to determine the level of benefit it wishes to provide.

Plan Administration and Maintenance

After the plan is in place, the practice must fulfill its responsibilities under the plan, such as ensuring that various reports are filed and distributed on a regular basis. This normally involves hiring a third-party administrator, but the practice and the trustees are ultimately responsible for ensuring that these functions are in compliance with all applicable laws.

The practice administrator generally coordinates internal compliance and related communications with third-party vendors. Employees must complete enrollment forms in connection with their plan participation, which typically include their election to participate, their investment direction (if self-directed), and a designation of beneficiary form.

Contributions, including employee deferrals, must be deposited into the plan on a regular basis. Finally, the practice should continually evaluate its plan design and investment process and performance to ensure that the plan continues to satisfy the goals of the physician-owners and the employees.

Legal Documents

Continual updates and modifications of tax laws and other legislation require that plan documents be reviewed at least annually. In the case of a prototype plan, the company that sponsors the prototype generally coordinates all necessary amendments and communications with participants and government agencies. If the practice has an individually designed plan, it will need its attorney or other retirement plan professional to draft the necessary amendments to the plan and complete the other required actions. If the practice has an ongoing relationship with this attorney or outside advisor, they will generally inform the practice when these amendments are required.

Practices with a safe harbor 401(k) plan should provide notice to the participants of the intention to fund the plan and the method of contribution to be used (as previously discussed). This is generally necessary for the plan to meet the safe harbor requirements and eliminate the nondiscrimination testing.

Reporting Requirements

Participants are legally required to receive adequate plan information on a regular basis. Initially, they should be provided with a summary plan description (an abbreviated version of the legal documents that describe how the plan operates on a day-to-day basis). They should also receive appropriate notification when the plan is amended or restated. If the practice has a safe harbor 401(k) plan, it also needs to provide the participants notice each year, as described earlier.

Plan participants should receive regular statements that summarize the financial transactions occurring in their accounts, including employer and employee funding, and transfers between investments and income (realized and unrealized gains and losses). They must also receive a copy of the plan's annual report, which is typically prepared by the third-party administrator.[24]

For most plans, the practice must file IRS Form 5500, Annual Return/Report of Employee Benefit Plan. Although this is an IRS form, it is a consolidated return that meets the requirements of the IRS, the DOL, and the Pension Benefit Guaranty Corporation.[25]

Administrative Services, Record-Keeping, and Investment Management

In most cases, an employer or plan sponsor retains the services of a third-party administrator to assist in complying with the legal requirements of the plan. Typically, the third-party administrator completes the compliance services required for the plan, including any testing or reporting requirements. The practice should take particular care in selecting a firm to perform those services to ensure compliance with regulatory agencies and also to receive proper service and expertise. Depending on where and how the assets are invested, the third-party administrator may or may not serve as the record-keeper and provide the necessary quarterly or annual participant statements.

Larger group practices may hire accountants and actuaries to provide these functions internally. Practices should compare the costs of using third parties with those of hiring qualified employees. Even practices that handle plan administration services internally may have to hire external third-party administrators or actuaries to provide consulting services for the group in order to ensure compliance.

New Participant Paperwork

Within the 30- to 90-day period prior to the time employees become participants in the plan, they should receive certain information regarding the plan. The new participants will need a copy of the summary plan description and, if applicable, any safe harbor notices.

Each participant must complete a form designating beneficiaries, which is provided by the service provider who drafts the plan document.

In general, married individuals must name their spouse as their beneficiary unless the spouse signs a form that provides consent otherwise. This can help avoid potential problems if the participant dies. For example, a participant might name a child as a beneficiary without considering who the guardian might be or list a group such as "all my children" rather than providing specific names.

As discussed earlier, if the practice has a 401(k) plan, the participant has to complete a form selecting the amount of their deferral contribution and authorizing the related payroll deduction. For self-directed plans, the practice may need documentation of the participants' selected investments.

Contributions

The practice has to ensure that it deposits all plan contributions in a timely manner. This includes employer contributions and employee contributions, such as deferrals and loan repayments.

The practice must generally pay employer contributions to the plan no later than the due date of its tax return, including extensions. For corporate entities, the due date is two and one-half months following the end of the year. For partnerships, limited liability entities, and sole proprietorships, this due date is three and one-half months following the end of the year. All entities may apply for an automatic six-month extension. (For a discussion regarding cash flow issues regarding timing of retirement plan contributions, see the *Financial Management* volume in the MGMA Body of Knowledge Review series.)

ERISA regulations require that the practice deposit employee contributions as soon as possible, but no later than the 15th business day of the month following the month in which these amounts were withheld from the employees' pay. In at least one court case, the court was not lenient: An employer that failed to deposit elective deposits within two business days after they were withheld was deemed to have made a fiduciary breech. IRS Form 5500 contains a question about whether these payments have been made in a timely manner.

The DOL is stricter about deposits of employee loan repayments to the plan. They claim that the deferral deposit standard rule of the 15th business day of the following month does not hold, and those deposits should be made as soon as they can be reasonably segregated from the practice's assets.[26]

Distributions

The practice must properly handle participant distributions. Most of the time these are distributions to terminated participants or their beneficiaries; however, the practice may also have to make distributions to current employees who have reached the age at which they must take required distributions (currently age 70½).

A practice should pay distributions to terminated employees according to its plan documents and all applicable regulations. It should provide a notice to the terminated employee or beneficiary explaining the tax rules regarding the distribution, such as the rollover option and federal income tax withholding on taxable distributions. The IRS has written a model notice that employers may use for this purpose.[27] Third-party administrators or other advisors usually provide the required forms and notices.

The participant or beneficiary may elect a direct rollover of the contribution to an IRA or other qualified retirement plan and avoid paying current income taxes on the distribution.

If the participant or beneficiary elects to receive the distribution, the practice must generally withhold 20 percent of the distribution as federal income taxes. Unless the participant or beneficiary rolls the gross amount of this distribution over to an IRA or other qualified plan within 60 days, the distribution will be taxable income to that individual. Participants who are younger than 59½ years of age and are not disabled must generally pay an additional 10 percent early distribution penalty.

No distributions should be made from the plan without signed distribution documents from the participant. In most cases, the third-party administrator or record-keeper assists the employer in the distribution process.

Plan Monitoring and Ongoing Assessment

Plan trustees should ensure that the appropriate tools are in place to monitor the continued successful operation of the retirement plan. A practice should regularly evaluate plan investment performance, such as by comparing the return on investment to major indices.

The trustees' fiduciary responsibility includes proper and prudent investment of plan assets, even when it uses outside investment managers. The key to monitoring and assessment of the plan is the process used, not necessarily the end result.

Tax laws can change, as can the practice's needs. The trustees should periodically evaluate the structure of their existing plan to determine whether it best meets their current needs.

Conclusion

Effective management of staff compensation and benefits is a key component in providing quality patient care and supporting the ongoing financial health of the medical practice. The key knowledge and skills required to accomplish this role include evaluating and overseeing implementation of a wide range of employee benefits, benchmarking employee compensation packages against other employers, and ensuring that compensation is efficiently administered.

Notes

1. Stephen L. Wagner, "Defining the ACMPE Fellow," *College View* (Fall 2003): 27–30.
2. U.S. Congressional Budget Office, *Updated Estimates of the Effects of the Insurance Coverage Provisions of the Affordable Care Act* (Washington, DC: U.S. Congressional Budget Office, Health and Human Resources Division, April 2014), www.cbo.gov/sites/default/files/45231-ACA_Estimates.pdf.
3. Geoffrey Kollmann, "Social Security: Summary of Major Changes in the Cash Benefits Program," CRS Legislative Histories 2, May 18, 2000, www.socialsecurity.gov/history/reports/crsleghist2.html.
4. Thomas J. Stanley and William D. Danko, *The Millionaire Next Door* (Atlanta: Longstreet Press, 1996), 74–77.
5. "Meeting Your Fiduciary Responsibilities," U.S. Department of Labor, www.dol.gov/ebsa/publications/fiduciaryresponsibility.html.
6. Kevin J. Donovan, "Defined Benefit Plan Design," in *The CPA's Guide to Retirement Plans for Small Businesses*, ed. Gary S. Lesser (New York: American Institute of Certified Public Accountants, 2004), 217–218.
7. Alicia H. Munnell, Francesca Golub-Sass, and Anthony Webb, "What Moves the National Retirement Risk Index? A Look Back and an Update," An Issue in Brief: Center for Retirement Research at Boston College, January 2007, Number 2007-1, 4.
8. Donovan, "Defined Benefit Plan Design."

9. Richard A. Naegele and Kelly Ann VanDenHaute, "Tax Qualified Retirement Plans and Fringe Benefits," in *Physician Practice Management: Essential Operational and Financial Knowledge*, ed. Lawrence F. Wolper (Burlington, MA: Jones & Bartlett Learning, 2013), 538.
10. Naegele and VanDenHaute, "Tax Qualified Retirement Plans and Fringe Benefits," 536.
11. Lawrence C. Starr, "Internal Revenue Code Section 401(k) and Safe Harbor 401(k) Plan Design," in *The CPA's Guide to Retirement Plans for Small Businesses*, ed. Gary S. Lesser (New York: American Institute of Certified Public Accountants, 2004), 189–191.
12. Naegele and VanDenHaute, "Tax Qualified Retirement Plans and Fringe Benefits," 539.
13. Naegele and VanDenHaute, "Tax Qualified Retirement Plans and Fringe Benefits," 541.
14. Naegele and VanDenHaute, "Tax Qualified Retirement Plans and Fringe Benefits," 539.
15. Gary S. Lesser, "ERISA Fiduciary Considerations," in *The CPA's Guide to Retirement Plans for Small Businesses*, ed. Gary S. Lesser (New York: American Institute of Certified Public Accountants, 2004): 474–475.
16. Naegele and VanDenHaute, "Tax Qualified Retirement Plans and Fringe Benefits," 538.
17. Fred Reish, Bruce Ashton, and Gary Ammon, "Fiduciary Investment Advice for Participants," Client Alert, Employee Benefits & Executive Compensation Practice Group, DrinkerBiddle, December 2011, www.raymondjames.com/Branches/c2c/35t/keogh/pdf/Fiduciary_Investment_Advice_for_Participants.pdf.
18. Lesser, "ERISA Fiduciary Considerations," 476.
19. Naegele and VanDenHaute, "Tax Qualified Retirement Plans and Fringe Benefits," 543.
20. Lesser, "ERISA Fiduciary Considerations," 10–11.
21. Lesser, "ERISA Fiduciary Considerations," 135–161.
22. Naegele and VanDenHaute, "Tax Qualified Retirement Plans and Fringe Benefits,"537.
23. Lesser, "ERISA Fiduciary Considerations," 165–167.
24. "Consumer Information on Health Plans," U.S. Department of Labor, www.dol.gov/ebsa/consumer_info_health.html.
25. "Instructions for Form 5500: Annual Return/Report of Employee Benefit Plan," Internal Revenue Service, 2014, www.dol.gov/ebsa/pdf/2014-5500 inst.pdf, page 1.
26. Lesser, "ERISA Fiduciary Considerations," 389–393.
27. Internal Revenue Service, "401(k) Resource Guide - Plan Participants—General Distribution Rules," August 14, 2014, www.irs.gov/Retirement-Plans/Plan-Participant,-Employee/401k-Resource-Guide-Plan-Participants-General-Distribution-Rules.

Chapter 5

Managing and Evaluating Staff Performance

Managing Performance

The performance management system, which includes performance planning, evaluation, and rating, is a vital component of human resource management. It is perhaps the most important and sometimes most troublesome aspect of the employer–employee relationship. The key skills required to effectively manage this system include:

- Implementing a performance management review system, including performance standards, professional development plans, goal-setting, schedule for periodic reviews, and evaluation tools;
- Setting appropriate expectations for performance and behavior; and
- Developing an incentive program.

The results of the performance management process are used to establish individual goals and objectives; award appropriate salary increases; identify promotional, transfer, and training opportunities; and determine potential disciplinary and termination actions. Often this aspect of managing is the most vulnerable point of the employment relationship, generating the most complaints about management functions. These complaints occur because many performance evaluation systems are too subjective and result in inconsistent management decisions based on arbitrary judgments and evaluations. Vague and poorly defined performance criteria lend themselves to biased judgments and evaluations, and litigation. Therefore, it is critical that employers have a performance management system that accurately measures and improves employee performance and is legally defensible.

The impetus for developing an effective performance management process is very clear. Salaries and wages compose as much as 60 to 70 percent of a healthcare organization's total operating costs. There is a clear link between the successful organizational operation and the effective and efficient performance of its employees. A comprehensive performance management process can help the organization attract and retain highly qualified employees and ensure quality, cost-effective service. As a result, both employee and employer goals are achieved.

As patient expectations and demands increase, the quality of performance — whether of a physician, nurse, or other staff member — must also increase. Total quality performance management becomes more vital. To maintain and expand the current patient and financial base, medical practices need a performance management process that is contemporary, easy to administer, and effective.

Managers and staff often have misguided and counterproductive beliefs about why organizations should use performance management systems in the first place. Many of these beliefs result from managers and supervisors using poorly designed performance evaluation forms that focus on judging the employee as a person, rather than evaluating the employee's job performance and behavior. Some employees feel that their performance reviews reflect more of a parent–child relationship where the supervisor scolds the employee for poor performance. This awkward situation causes tension and distress for both the employee and the supervisor.

An effective performance management system involves management planning, organization, leading, and controlling performance. It results in increased productivity and more engaged employees. Supervisors are expected to have insights into which goals to set, how to achieve those goals, how to organize work efforts appropriately, how to lead workers in the right direction, and how to monitor and control performance so that it stays on target to reach practice goals.

Consider the word *performance* in performance management. This is what management is all about: supervisors plan, organize, lead, and control performance. An effective performance management process enhances each of those tasks and results in improved productivity. Supervisors are expected to have insight into what goals to set, how to achieve those goals, how to organize work efforts appropriately, how to lead workers in the right direction, and how to monitor and control performance so that it stays on target.

An effective performance management process encompasses six components. These are:

1. Organizational goals and objectives;
2. An individual's performance and planning;
3. Employee performance measurements;
4. Performance reviews;
5. Ongoing feedback and coaching; and
6. Recognition and rewards.

The medical group should emphasize performance expectations up front, reinforce them consistently, and reward results regularly. Your group should provide a uniform and general framework for performance management, which ensures that employees know what is expected of them and supervisors know how to establish a job-related basis for planning, managing, and evaluating performance.

Performance Planning

Federal and state statutes do not mandate performance evaluations for private employees, and an employer generally cannot be held liable for failure to give an employee a performance assessment. There are, however, expectations. If an employer makes a promise, either oral or written, to an employee that he or she will receive an evaluation but the employee does not receive an evaluation, the employer could, in theory, be found liable under a breach of contract. The employee relied on the employer's promise, but the employer broke the promise and therefore the employee was harmed.

Most often, promises of performance evaluations are written in an employment offer letter, an employment contract, or in the employee handbook. Likewise, during new employee orientation or onboarding, employees are told by the person training them that their performance will be evaluated by their supervisor. Either way, the medical practice has promised to evaluate an employee's performance.

If your employee handbook states that "Employees will receive annual performance evaluations," that statement could create an enforceable right to a performance evaluation. Conversely, a slight wording change can have important legal ramifications. If the employee handbook states that "Employees should receive annual performance evaluations," a court is much more likely to rule that an annual performance review is not a right of the employee but rather a goal of the employer. You should review the practice's employment offer letters, employment contracts, and employee handbooks to eliminate any language that may obligate the practice to give performance evaluations.

There are several pitfalls that the practice's management and supervisors can avoid to protect the practice from legal issues regarding performance management issues. Management can protect the practice by:

- Developing and implementing a sound performance system;
- Providing training about the system;
- Enforcing the use of the system;
- Ensuring appropriate use of the system and relevant policies and procedures; and
- Requiring legal consultation and advice before discharging an employee.

Supervisors can help protect the practice from any legal ramifications by:

- Paying careful attention to performance planning;
- Giving adequate performance feedback to employees all the time, not just during the official performance evaluation process;
- Observing and correcting performance problems immediately;
- Thoughtfully and thoroughly completing the required performance evaluation forms;
- Completing regular evaluations in a timely manner;
- Being honest and thorough in performance feedback;

- Not inflating performance ratings; and
- Taking the performance management systems seriously.

Evaluating Performance

Measuring and evaluating an employee's performance enables practice management to determine if the employee achieved or exceeded expectations and goals. Managers and supervisors can use this information to better understand, manage, and help improve the employee's performance. Evaluating employees gives supervisors the information about how their employees are doing and what, if any, issues need to be resolved in order to increase performance and productivity. This information also helps supervisors make intelligent decisions about recognition and rewards, promotions, development opportunities, employee discipline, if needed, and possible termination.

Evaluating performance gives employees a chance to receive constructive feedback about their performance and make changes if necessary. It also provides employees with the opportunity to discuss with their supervisor any possible issues, challenges, or problems that might hinder their performance.

Performance Evaluation Tools

Some of the more common performance evaluation tools are described in the following sections. For a more detailed explanation, please refer to the Medical Group Management Association (MGMA®) book, *HR Policies and Procedures*.[1]

Critical Incident Rating

The critical incident rating approach is based on an appraiser's written observation of an employee's performance throughout a designated time period. The supervisor maintains a log to record an employee's performance during work incidents that are considered critical, such as dealing with a patient. These critical incidents are sometimes called *significant occurrences*. This performance log should contain examples of both satisfactory and unsatisfactory performance.

The critical incident report relies heavily on the supervisor's verbal skills. Although the report has the advantage of being job related, it can be biased by the incidents the supervisor chooses to record. It is a common mistake to record only incidents that the supervisor finds unsatisfactory. Supervisors forget to record incidents of exceptional performance because, in reality, they expect that type of behavior.

If done correctly, this approach can be very time consuming for the supervisor, requiring constant note taking and close observation. Employees consider such constant observation as micromanagement. Employees dislike having someone looking over their shoulders all day.

One positive use of this approach is to amplify specific job-related examples when using other formats. The approach is most useful, however, when dealing with performance problems. Documentation of critical incidents is a vital step in developing a performance improvement plan or preparing to discipline or terminate an employee.

Peer Review

The peer review method was originally designed for rating professional employees. It is frequently used in medical practices by and for physicians. In this process, a panel of colleagues confidentially rates each employee's performance. One of the main benefits of this system is that it allows for a credible rating by equals of a highly sophisticated workforce.

Many healthcare organizations are redesigning peer and coworker reviews so they can be used by any work group to evaluate employees in terms of performance factors such as patient relations, teamwork, and quality. In time, coworker reviews may become an integral part of the total performance plan and evaluation process. The medical group will base these reviews on its own defined performance factors and standards.

There are several performance evaluation tools that require the evaluator to compare employees. These include:

- *Paired comparison ranking,* which involves comparing each employee in a job to all other employees in the group;
- *Alternation ranking,* which involves evaluating all workers in a job group against a standard measure; and
- *Forced distribution ranking,* which involves ranking employees on a universal measure according to a fixed proportion of the entire group.

One disadvantage of the ranking approach is that it focuses on the group rather than on the individual. It does not recognize that each person has a different level of experience in the job, has different strengths and weaknesses, and may be on a different development path. Most important, ranking fails to identify individual differences in performance or inform the individual employee about how performance can be improved.

360-Degree Evaluation

The 360-degree evaluation is a popular approach used by all types of businesses. This approach involves getting evaluations from a variety of people who interact with an employee. It usually includes supervisors, coworkers, and staff from different departments who interact with the employee on a regular basis, such as subordinates, customers, suppliers, and others. This type of evaluation also requires that the employee complete a self-evaluation using the same format that other evaluators use.

The purpose of the 360-degree review is to achieve more accurate feedback related to overall performance. It can highlight areas of needed improvement that prevent other workers from performing their duties. Implementing 360-degree reviews is not difficult if your group already uses a form of peer reviews. These reviews can be done on paper or online through secured access in the group's intranet. Once all questionnaires have been distributed to specific parties, completed, and submitted, the direct supervisor or a human resource representative tallies the scores, develops a performance improvement plan, and discusses the results with the employee. The results are given to the direct supervisor for review with the employee.

Performance Standard

A performance standard method can be used successfully as both a planning and evaluation tool. It focuses on general job-related factors that are applicable among all employees or across specific groups. This method is useful in reinforcing the performance factors that are important to a medical practice.

Factor definitions should be stated in behavioral language; for example, "Patient relations: Display of respect, patience, helpfulness to patients, friendly manner, appropriate acknowledgment of patient feelings, ability to deal with clients in a nondefensive manner." Legally, it is unacceptable to use personality traits or attitudes as performance criteria. The focus must be on performance factors that are specific and critical to the job.

Once the medical practice has determined the factors it values, the tool can be used for all employees, including management. This format allows for tailoring to each job. The supervisors should add two to four performance standards and behavioral comments that are directly related to each employee's job. All factors should be discussed and agreed on by the supervisor and the employee.

Performance measurement standards should be expressed in specific, measurable terms (e.g., quantity, quality, time, and cost). In addition, they should be both realistic and challenging.

A simple rating scale can be used with a performance standard tool. The rating scale can be numerical (e.g., from 1 being "unacceptable" to 5 being "outstanding"). The preferred approach is to scale by four levels (e.g., does not meet standard, meets standard, above standard, and exceeds standard). The word *standard* reinforces the concept of a performance standard of success. It does not mean average. Instead, it means fully acceptable, competent, proficient, or hitting the mark.

Once the factors and standards have been finalized, the supervisor implements the tool for performance planning immediately. For example, a new employee would not only receive a copy of his or her job description, but also a copy of the performance plan. The supervisor would explain the expectations, with modifications made to fit the new employee's skill and experience level. With all employees, the supervisor and employee can use the tool to plan performance for the next period.

The performance standard approach takes little time to develop and use, and it does not require extensive verbal skills. However, a rating by itself does not inform employees of their deficiencies or motivate them to improve their performance. Therefore, if this method is used, supervisors should include a descriptive comment about each performance factor to clarify the rating at evaluation time. The group practice could select six to ten performance standards for each job and then have the supervisor add two to four performance standards that are job specific for each staff member.

This approach also requires the assignment of an *importance weight* to each factor; that is, each factor is assigned a numerical value that reflects its importance in overall job performance. For example, quality might be given a weight of 50 percent. It is important for employees to know how important each factor is or what counts most. Again, this should be discussed at the beginning of each performance period to ensure that the supervisor and employee agree on the priorities.

This method takes some upfront time to develop in that supervisors must specify significant performance factors, the related standards, and the relative weights. However, once the tool is developed, it is easy to use. It is a common-sense approach that facilitates effective communication between the supervisor and employee.

Criterion-Based Method

The criterion-based approach is another recommended option. It features more specific descriptions of performance factors. It can be used both as a planning tool at the start of the year and as an evaluation tool.

The criterion approach focuses on clearly defined criteria and standards. A criterion is a specific area of job performance that is used to evaluate an employee's performance.

A performance standard in a criterion-based approach is represented by a series of performance levels. Each level correlates to a particular performance rating for the criterion. For example, a rate of return on investment that is 0 to 3 percent might be rated as "does not meet standard."

The performance standard in this tool is a measurement device that is very specific so that performance expectations are very clear. The measurements should relate to quantity, quality, timeliness, and financial parameters. They should be expressed in numerical or behavioral terms to ensure validity and reliability.

Goal Setting

A goal-setting system involves negotiation between the supervisor and employee to establish performance objectives. It is used at the beginning of a performance period, which might be the probationary or training period or a complete year.

One widely used technique is management by objectives (MBO). This technique involves mutual goal setting between supervisors and employees. The employee aims to meet the agreed-on goals within a determined time period.

The MBO approach usually involves:

- A job review and goal-setting agreement by the supervisor and employee;
- Development of performance standards by both;
- A reality check to ensure that the objectives are achievable (i.e., that resources are available and that the employee has control over the outcome); and
- Ongoing discussion throughout the time period concerning the employee's performance in regard to the established objectives.

The main strength of the MBO approach is that it focuses on the organization's goals and objectives. It is directly tied to the strategic plan, so employees know how their performance will affect the organization's success. In addition, employee input is stressed to improve commitment and performance.

One major drawback to the MBO process is that it may not work well for all types of jobs. For example, it may be difficult to tie the performance of a medical records clerk to specific organizational objectives.

The MBO approach may also concentrate too heavily on results, ignoring the methods required to achieve the objectives. That is, it may become a matter of "winning the war, but killing all the troops in the process." It is also a time-consuming process because the supervisor must invest considerable time negotiating with each employee.

Variations of the MBO approach, where job goals are less directly tied to specific organizational objectives, offer considerable merit to medical practices. A goal-setting format that works well is one focused on major accountabilities related to the job description. In this approach, three to six major accountabilities are identified. The supervisor and employee negotiate expected results in terms of objectives and measurable standards. These may be weighted to indicate priority.

Choosing an Evaluation Tool

Some practices choose to use the same evaluation tool for all employees regardless of job function or exempt or nonexempt status. Other practices identify key performance factors that are mandatory for all employees (e.g., patient satisfaction) and then add other performance factors for specific job duties and responsibilities. Using separate evaluation forms for management and nonmanagement is strongly recommended. This is an effective way of reinforcing performance factors that pertain to management such as leadership, creativity, innovation, decision making, fiscal responsibility, and strategic planning.

Physician Performance Evaluation

In many healthcare organizations, physicians and practice managers either ignore evaluating physician performance or talk about it but never implement it. There is little published in medical literature about the design and implementation of physician performance evaluation systems. It's almost as if physician performance evaluation is a taboo topic and/or a legacy of the autonomy that physicians have enjoyed in the past. This could be because physician performance evaluation is challenging and multidimensional because of the complexity of their job responsibilities, their skepticism about the process, and the difficulties of critiquing peers with whom they work closely.

However, there is an increasing emphasis on evaluating physician performance because it directly affects the quality and cost of patient care, which affects the success and profitability of any healthcare organization. In our rapidly changing environment, the demands for high-quality care and physician accountability is an essential core component of effective healthcare management. These trends, along with the increasing number of employed physicians, explain why more healthcare providers are beginning to focus on assessing the complex components of physician performance.

Healthcare organizations that do evaluate physician performance frequently use some type of a peer review process. However, peer performance reviews have an underlying philosophy of camaraderie rather than providing objective and constructive feedback. Physician performance evaluation forms have primarily concentrated on assessing clinical competencies rather than behavioral competencies. Clinical competencies include knowledge and proficiency of technical skills, billing and chart analysis to assess patient outcomes, the number of procedures performed, physician adherence to procedural guidelines, and so on.

A blended approach that addresses both clinical and behavioral competencies is more effective for evaluating physician performance. Behavioral competencies focus on interpersonal skills and fit with the organization's vision, mission, and culture. They include effective communication skills and clinical reasoning, as well as using good judgment, managing emotions, showing empathy, and establishing good relationships with patients and their families. Rarely does a physician performance evaluation form reflect the importance of behavioral skills that are more difficult to evaluate and often ignored.

To address this issue, MGMA published the *Physician Job Description Toolkit*[2] to help practices and other healthcare organizations develop or redesign a physician performance evaluation system. The book includes physician performance templates for both evaluation and self-evaluation.

Promotions and Transfers

Employees are often an overlooked resource to fill internal positions. The practice knows more about its current staff's work history, performance, and potential than it does about new recruits. Often the high costs of recruiting, orienting, and training new employees can be saved by promoting competent employees — those who already have demonstrated their loyalty, stability, and work performance — to higher-level jobs.

The hope of a promotion to a better job and a chance for a salary increase are very important to most employees, so a promotion-from-within policy can be an effective motivator. Employees will strive to do their best and often obtain additional training and/or education to increase their chances of being promoted. Depending on the level of the vacant position, it can take six months to a year for a new employee to become fully productive. Because current employees are already familiar with the medical practice and its staff, they must only learn the new job duties and responsibilities.

When current employees are promoted, they are able to perform several jobs, which creates a more flexible and cross-trained workforce. Also, when they are promoted, their lower-level vacant jobs may be easier to fill. The practice should fill each position with the best-qualified person. Keep in mind that promoting from within builds morale and usually increases productivity. However, in today's climate of high unemployment and economic uncertainty, employees are more reluctant to leave their jobs, so promotional opportunities may not be as available as they were in the past. Therefore cross-training, job enhancement, and promoting from within have become a major focus for employers.

Implementing a Promotion Program

The human resource specialist should coordinate your promotion program. Supervisors and managers usually will not oppose promotions, but they are often unaware of qualified employees who might be eligible for and interested in a promotion. To be effective and respected by employees, support for the promotion program must begin with top management. Effective promotion program elements include:

- Job posting;
- Job bidding;
- Use of employee records;
- Skills inventory;
- Staff coordination;
- Good record-keeping; and
- Employee development programs.

These elements are crucial to recruiting present employees for job openings in your medical group.

Implementing a Transfer Program

Transfers are another good way to fill vacant positions, especially in larger organizations. Transfers can happen in one of two ways:

1. Management-mandated transfers; and
2. Employee-requested transfers.

A medical practice can require employees to move to a different department or a different role within the organization. Practice management may mandate a transfer because of:

- Fluctuations in department workloads;
- Variations in department production flow; and
- More efficient use of employees' skills and abilities.

Usually, an employee will accept a transfer to a new position at the same salary, assuming that the same skills or previously acquired skills are used. In all cases, management should retain the right to transfer employees, regardless of whether they agree with the transfer. Three criteria that should be considered when deciding whether to transfer an employee are:

1. The employee's ability to perform the new job;
2. Whether his or her performance was satisfactory in the former job; and
3. The salary grade of the new position compared to the former one.

Sometimes an employee has difficulty performing his or her present duties because of personality differences with the present supervisor, the working dynamics of the department, or a conflict with another staff member. Under these circumstances, the employee can request a transfer to another position. If approved, management should determine if the previous supervisor, coworkers, or surroundings were the cause of the work difficulties rather than a lack of ability to perform the job. In this way, turnover can be reduced, and ultimately, the employee will be happier and more productive in the new position.

When an employee requests a transfer, the designated human resource professional or the practice administrator should determine the reason for the request. If the reason is caused by personality conflicts with supervisors or coworkers, practice management and the human resource professional should work with both the employee and the employee's supervisor to see if a compromise can be reached, keeping the employee in the current position.

In other cases, the employee may think that a change of atmosphere, an opportunity to advance in a different type of work, or a different set of working conditions that may be available in another department is needed. It is in the practice's best interest to try to help an employee find a new position within the practice. If there is a vacant position, the employee requesting a transfer should apply to the open position just as any other employee or applicant would. An employee-requested transfer may not be possible if there is not an open position for which the requesting employee is qualified.

Promotion and Transfer Program Elements

Promotion and transfer programs begin by establishing a process to post job vacancies on message boards, bulletin boards, on job-recruiting Websites, or through e-mail to inform current employees of openings. The job posting should include a brief description of the job duties, responsibilities, qualifications, and the hiring supervisor or manager. The employee should submit a résumé and complete the practice's application form to be considered for the position.

Job Bidding

Job bidding is another procedure that may be used where interested employees complete an employee job bid form and submit it to the designated human resource professional or to the administrator. The job bidding system should be open to all full- and part-time employees working at least 20 hours per week. In most cases, employees should be employed by the practice for at least six consecutive months before being considered for a promotional opportunity. A current skills inventory of your present staff is an effective method for locating an internal employee eligible for promotion or transfer and is coordinated by the designated human resource professional. Information on employees' skills, education, training, and interests can be pulled from a database or from employees' records and evaluated.

Assign someone to be responsible for coordinating the practice's promotion and transfer program. This person can counsel employees who are interested in transfers or promotions, or who are considering resigning to obtain a position outside the practice.

Miscellaneous Considerations

An effective promotion and transfer program relies on good employee records. This helps practices report results to the Equal Employment Opportunity Commission, if necessary. Managers should also publicize any efforts to promote employees. The practice should keep statistics on the number and kinds of employees who are either transferred or promoted each year. Reviewing and analyzing the results contributes to the continual success of the program.

Highly motivated, productive, and efficient employees are a valuable commodity. Supervisors should urge outstanding employees to seek promotions. The practice should also do its best to accommodate employees requesting a transfer to keep top talent in the practice. The practice should encourage its supervisors and managers to endorse your promotion and transfer program and refrain from blocking transfers and promotions of qualified employees. A supervisor or manager who permits and encourages upward mobility builds a motivated and productive staff.

Legal Considerations

Employment policies concerning the promotion or transfer of employees must comply with Title VII of the Civil Rights Act of 1964 as amended, the Americans with Disabilities Act of 1990, the Age Discrimination in Employment Act of 1967, the Genetic Information Nondiscrimination Act of 2008, and state and local nondiscrimination laws. Thus promotion and transfer policies should be written to ensure that they do not have the intent, purpose, or effect of unlawfully discriminating against any employee because of race, color, religion, national origin, gender, disability, age, genetic information, or any other status protected by federal, state, or local law. In addition, a transfer may be considered a reasonable accommodation for a qualified individual with a disability under the Americans with Disabilities Act.

The *Uniform Guidelines on Employee Selection Procedures*[3] requires that tests used to select employees for promotion be predictive of or significantly correlated with important elements of job performance. Under the regulations issued by the Office of Federal Contract Compliance Programs, posting job openings by the employer is an important part of any affirmative action program designed to upgrade female and minority employees and to ensure that people with disabilities have equal employment opportunities.

Promotion and Transfer Policy

Your medical practice's promotion and transfer policy needs to establish promotion guidelines to follow when a position becomes vacant. Promotion decisions should generally be based on merit, work record, and selected examinations when appropriate. Seniority should be considered only if two or more applicants for the same job are equally qualified. The right to transfer or reassign employees when reasonably necessary is management's decision. In the absence of a written policy establishing transfer procedures, employees will often attempt to negotiate a transfer directly with a supervisor rather than with the appropriate manager. An employee requesting a transfer should follow the same procedures when applying for open positions as employees seeking promotions.

Temporary transfers may be necessary to meet temporary work overloads, address a staff shortage, avoid overtime, and prevent the need to hire temporary help. Transfers may include a change in the work days, hours, or location.

A time limit for accepting applications or job bids should be set for every job opening. When promoting or transferring employees, the practice runs the risk of the employee being unable to satisfactorily perform the job. For this reason, many implement a six-month training period. If the employee fails to perform the new job satisfactorily, your policy should state whether he or she will be reinstated to the former position or to a comparable position, if one is available.

Employee Discipline

Discipline has two purposes. First, it is training and learning how to successfully fulfill one's job duties and responsibilities. Second, and more traditionally, it is action taken by the employer against an employee for either poor performance or a violation of the organization's policies and/or rules. The objective of disciplinary action is generally to remedy a problem. To fulfill this objective, management must establish standards of appropriate conduct, a procedure for evaluating behavior, and a system for administering disciplinary action.

Disciplinary systems may follow different approaches, but regardless of the approach, all disciplinary systems and policies should make clear that the employer has a right to immediately terminate an employee at any time without warning and for any reason or no reason. Preventive discipline is one approach that seeks to heighten employees' awareness of organization rules and policies to avoid infractions and motivate employees to perform their jobs effectively. When improper behavior occurs, management stresses the importance of improvement and offers constructive suggestions and training.

Other disciplinary systems use penalties appropriate to the specific infraction and circumstances. Such systems usually consist of various potential actions depending on the seriousness of the problematic conduct or performance and whether it has occurred before, including verbal reprimand, written reprimand, suspension, demotion, and dismissal.

Your disciplinary policy should attempt to meet the following objectives:

- Establish a procedure to inform your employees of below-standard conduct or performance;
- Provide a means by which the employee is given warning and counseling, as appropriate, ensuring that he or she understands what is expected;
- Provide appropriate disciplinary action; and
- Reserve the employer's right to immediately terminate an employee at any time, with or without warning and with or without reason.

The practice's supervisors and managers are the keys to a successful disciplinary system. They are responsible for enforcing the rules and taking the appropriate action when violations occur. The designated human resource professional should approve and monitor all disciplinary actions to ensure consistency because occasionally supervisors may abuse their authority or be unaware of how a disciplinary matter was previously handled. That is one key reason why your employee disciplinary policy should be written. Equally important is training all supervisors and managers about how to implement it.

It is important to ensure that your disciplinary policy allows for immediate termination. Employers should not promise *progressive discipline,* which is a series of progressive steps the employer will follow to discipline employees, because there will be situations where an employee should be terminated immediately.

Disciplinary Process Guidelines

Medical practices should attempt to deal constructively with employee performance problems, unsatisfactory behavior, and employee errors. The disciplinary process used should be determined by the practice in its discretion in light of the facts and circumstances of each case. Each situation will generally be considered in light of a variety of factors including, but not limited to:

- The seriousness of the situation;
- The employee's past conduct and length of service; and
- The nature of the employee's previous performance or incidents involving the employee.

Depending on the facts, disciplinary action may include oral or written warnings, probation, suspension with or without pay, or immediate discharge. With employees employed on an at-will basis, a practice and its employees both have the absolute power and authority to terminate the employment relationship at any time without notice and with or without reason or cause.

Legal Requirements

Employees who believe that they have been wrongfully disciplined or discharged, whether because of discrimination or otherwise, increasingly resort to litigation. Given the scope of potential damage awards and the cost of defending claims, healthcare employers are advised to develop discipline and discharge procedures that limit or control exposure to such litigation. When developing disciplinary guidelines, management must be fully committed to implementing the guidelines; otherwise, your disciplinary system could be unsuccessful and costly in terms of time and dollars.

Progressive Discipline

Corrective action strives to provide feedback to an employee to correct a behavior. Progressive discipline sets parameters on which behaviors are unacceptable and how the negative behaviors requiring change will be communicated with the employee.

Large medical groups usually have a progressive discipline process that clearly establishes expectations and consequences of those behaviors if not met. The discipline process may be different for the staff and physicians. The purpose of having a constructive discipline process is to establish guidelines that will ensure an environment that is efficient, productive, and orderly to provide standards and rules governing performance and a procedure for consistent, nondiscriminatory application of the rules with the intent of providing quality patient care. The policy does not apply to employees who are in their new-hire period or are per-diem or temporary employees. The personnel policy applies to part-time and full-time regular status employees.

Progressive discipline must be fair, consistent, well understood, and timely. Lack of a consistent process to administer discipline may ultimately lead to a disgruntled employee filing a lawsuit. A progressive discipline program provides the employee with feedback that clearly outlines unacceptable behavior and the consequences if this behavior is not changed.

Usually progressive discipline involves a verbal warning followed by a written warning. If behavior doesn't change, a suspension or final written warning is the next level of discipline. Ultimately, if behavior doesn't improve, the employee may be terminated.

Some behaviors may warrant a progressive level, and other behaviors may warrant more, or may skip a step and move into a higher level of discipline. For example, chronic tardiness would go through progressive discipline, whereas stealing money would result in immediate termination or suspension, pending an administrative investigation. Employees must understand that there is a process for discipline and consequences to bad behavior.

If a union is present in a practice, the union's progressive discipline process may require a union representative to be present with the union employee and manager when progressive discipline is administered.

Recorded Conference

For rule infractions considered less serious, a recorded conference may be the first step in the corrective action process. It consists of a verbal conference with, at a minimum, the employee and supervisor and will be documented in writing and placed in the employee's personnel file. Examples of behavior for which a recorded conference may be initiated as the first step of the correction action process include:

- Work area absence without permission (e.g., leaving work without clocking out);
- Extended lunch time or breaks without permission (e.g., taking a 30-minute break instead of a 15-minute break);
- Loitering during scheduled work time or during off-duty hours (e.g., staying in work area after shift and creating disturbances with employees);

- Smoking or eating in unauthorized areas (e.g., eating in surgical area that is a sterile environment);
- Conducting personal business on work premises (e.g., selling products during work time);
- Violation of parking rules (e.g., parking in a "no parking" or "patients only" zone for the duration of a work shift);
- Improper attire or appearance (e.g., wearing jeans or denim when not part of the dress code);
- Inefficiency or incompetence in work duties performed (e.g., failing to perform job duty during work shift);
- Unauthorized telephone use (e.g., making long-distance or extensive personal calls without permission); or
- Attendance problems (e.g., showing up late for work without prior notice or permission).

Written Corrective Action

The written corrective action is a document summarizing the performance problem or incident detrimental to the customer, inability to follow established policy, or the failure to respond to supervision. A written corrective action serves as notice that continued infractions will not be tolerated and/or that performance must improve to meet expectations. Examples of behavior for which a written corrective action is warranted include:

- Inappropriate treatment or behavior toward a customer;
- Conduct prejudicial to the best interest of the medical group;
- Careless, indifferent, or negligent job performance, including unsafe or unsanitary practices;
- Careless, neglectful, unauthorized, or improper use of company property or equipment;
- Collecting money or accepting gratuities for personal use;
- Failure of good behavior or neglect of duty; or
- Repeated or chronic infractions with no evident improvement in performance or conduct.

Suspension or Final Written Corrective Action

An unpaid suspension or final written corrective action in lieu of suspension may occur when performance continues to be detrimental to customer satisfaction or where a serious performance problem exists. Suspensions should be scheduled at a time as close to the infraction as possible but also so that patient care and consistency of service do not suffer. Depending on the seriousness of the incident or behavior, the employee may receive a suspension or final written corrective action as the first step of the corrective action process.

Examples of behavior warranting suspension include possession, use, or sale of alcohol, narcotics, or controlled substances on the medical group premises, or reporting to work under the influence of alcohol or narcotics, usually evidenced by one or more of the following behaviors:

- Inability to perform assigned work;
- Presentation of undesirable attributes (e.g., hygiene, attitude, uncooperativeness);
- Insubordination or refusal to perform a reasonable assignment after having been instructed by a supervisor to do so;
- Sleeping on the job;
- Disorderly conduct;
- Failure to conform to professional standards; or
- Any other critical failure of good behavior or serious neglect of duty.

Termination

Termination may occur as the final step in the corrective action process. Termination of an employee is never an easy task, but it is necessary if the employee does not consistently follow the medical group's policies and procedures. Termination may occur for serious offenses or for continued performance problems affecting the customer. Examples of behavior where immediate termination may be warranted include:

- Threat of or actual physical or verbal abuse of patients, visitors, employees;
- Inappropriate treatment of any patient for any reason;

- Falsification of any official medical group records (e.g., medical records);
- An illegal or dishonest act;
- Damage or theft of property;
- Absence from work without justifiable reason or, in some practices, without reporting off for two (or more, depending on the practice's variables) consecutive working days;
- Unauthorized possession, use, copying, or revealing of confidential information regarding patients, employees, or medical group activity;
- Unwelcome sexual advances, requests for sexual favors, or other verbal or physical conduct of a sexual nature with an employee, visitor, or patient;
- Harassment in any form, including that based on race, gender, religion, or national origin, which includes offensive jokes, ridicule, or racial, religious, sexual, or ethnic slurs;
- Improper use of leave of absence;
- Conviction of a felony relevant to the employee's position;
- Solicitation and/or distribution of literature (pornography, political campaigns, etc.); or
- Any other gross neglect of good behavior or gross neglect of duty.

Employee discharge, or firing, should generally be used when an employee has not corrected his or her behavior in response to disciplinary action or other correction attempts. However, immediate discharge should be used as necessary for things such as serious practice policy violations, including but not limited to unlawful harassment, violence, stealing, and embezzlement. Sometimes the only way to deal with poor employee performance or unsatisfactory conduct is to quickly end the employment relationship.

Discharging an employee is not easy emotionally or legally. To protect the practice from wrongful termination charges or litigation, you should attempt to rectify the situation, if possible, using coaching, counseling, and the practice's disciplinary process. Also work closely with the practice's legal counsel when making termination decisions.

General considerations for all discharges. You should consider the following questions when making discharge decisions. A "yes" answer to any of these questions does not mean that you should avoid discharging the employee. It means that you should carefully consider the risks involved and make an informed decision about termination. These questions are designed to allow you to conduct a risk assessment prior to proceeding with the decision to terminate.

- Were any representations made to the person that he or she was not employed as an at-will employee? If so, what were those representations?
- Is there a written offer of employment, a letter confirming the terms of the employment, an employment contract, or a collective bargaining agreement applicable to this employee?
- Will the discharge violate any public policy? For example, could the employee argue that the reason for discharge was the exercise of political beliefs, exercise of a statutory right, or the reporting of the employer to a government agency? Or, is there an outstanding or settled workers' compensation claim?
- Does the individual fit into a protected status (i.e., race, color, ethnicity, gender, national origin, religion, disability, age, veteran status, or other statuses that may be protected by state law, such as sexual orientation or marital status)?
- Has the individual made any protected complaints, such as complaints of unlawful discrimination or harassment, or whistleblowing complaints?
- Has the individual requested a reasonable accommodation for his or her religion or disability?
- Will the termination prevent the employee from vesting in the practice's pension, stock, or other bonuses in the immediate or foreseeable future?
- Has a thorough and proper investigation been conducted so that the decision is based on facts, rather than on subjective opinion, perception, hearsay, or speculation?
- Has the employee been given the opportunity to tell his or her side of the story?

- Are there extenuating circumstances or other mitigating factors that might justify disciplinary action rather than termination?
- Should the employee be suspended, pending further investigation?
- Is terminating this particular employee consistent with how the practice has treated other employees with similar behavioral or performance problems?
- Is the decision timely?
- Could this type of termination induce staff to seek union representation?
- Have you consulted with an employment attorney in order to fully assess possible risks and to assist you in making an informed decision?

Considerations for disciplinary discharges. In addition to the preceding general considerations, consider the following questions whenever you are contemplating a discharge as a disciplinary action:

- Was the violated rule or policy known to the employee? Was the policy or rule published? Is terminating this employee consistent with how you have applied the rule or policy to other employees who have engaged in similar behavior?
- Has this individual received disciplinary action in the past, such as a verbal warning, written warning, written reprimand, suspension, and so on?
- Did the employee have an opportunity to take corrective action?
- Are the witnesses, if any, credible?
- Was the information regarding the infraction obtained lawfully, such as a through drug or alcohol testing, private investigation, or a body or vehicle search?
- Is there proper documentation to support your decision?
- Does the employee's overall documented record support the decision, such as being consistently tardy, absent, uncooperative, or failing to correct behavior after receiving warnings?

- Is terminating this particular employee consistent with how the practice has treated other employees with similar behavioral problems or who have committed similar policy violations?

Considerations for poor performance discharges. In addition to the preceding general considerations, bear in mind the following questions whenever you are contemplating a discharge for poor performance:

- Do the prior and current performance evaluations support the decision?
- Was the employee not only told of the deficiencies, but also given sufficient time and opportunities to make the necessary improvements to meet expectations?
- Was the employee denied any requested training or other assistance to help with improvement?
- Is the cited reason for the discharge the real reason?
- Can the deficiency be measured objectively? Are the criticisms specific to the employee's actions, rather than to his or her attitude?
- Does the employee's overall documented record support the decision? For example, did the employee just receive an outstanding performance evaluation and a merit raise?
- Was the employee ever told that his or her failure to improve would result in termination?
- Is terminating this employee consistent with how the practice has treated other employees with similar performance deficiencies?

Method of discharge. Once the decision to discharge has been made, the practice needs to consider how the termination will happen. The following questions should be considered:

- Where will the meeting be conducted? It should be conducted in private.
- Who will lead the meeting? Usually the supervisor or manager should lead the meeting.
- Should a witness be present? Whenever possible, a witness should be present, preferably a human resource professional.

- Has the employee's computer access been discontinued?
- Has a checklist been prepared of what the employee needs to return to the employer, such as ID cards and keys?
- Has the employer prepared the final paycheck? Have any other payments, such as accrued vacation pay and expense reimbursements, been taken into account and included in the final paycheck in accordance with applicable law?
- Have appropriate steps been taken to protect the confidentiality of proprietary practice information and patients' private health information?
- Has anyone who has knowledge of the reasons for termination been instructed that this information should be treated as confidential? When asked for details about this employee's departure, individuals should state only that he or she is no longer with the practice.

Recognition and Reward Programs

The goal of recognition and reward programs is to positively reinforce the desired on-the-job behavior, improve employee morale, and contribute to employee retention. Medical practices with a highly participatory work environment that recognize and reward top performance outperform practices that do not. Some may rationalize that salaried employees who earn a competitive wage are paid enough and their salaries should be sufficient sources of motivation and recognition. But in reality, money sometimes does not have the desired effect of encouraging employees to do their best work or exceed job expectations.

Extra effort and increased commitment are generally associated more with how workers are treated than what they are paid. Studies dating as far back as the 1940s support this assertion, with employees consistently ranking factors such as interesting work, supervisors' appreciation, job security, and participation in decision making as being more important than their salaries.[4] Although money can be effective in some situations, it usually provides only a brief stimulus, whereas personal recognition and appreciation have longer-term positive effects.

Today, recognition and reward programs have replaced the traditional monetary reward system of the past.

This section briefly discusses ways to recognize and reward employees to build engagement and loyalty. For a more in-depth discussion about recognizing and rewarding employees, please refer to MGMA's *Acknowledge! Appreciate! Applaud! 172 Easy Ways to Reward Staff for Little or No Cost.*[5]

Types of Reward Programs

There are four distinct types of recognition and reward programs:

1. **Awareness.** Awareness focuses on being sensitive to coworkers and colleagues in the workplace. Welcoming body language such as direct eye contact when speaking with someone and smiling can help employees feel more valued. In addition, simple greetings at the beginning of the shift and pleasantries at the end of the shift can also encourage employees to perform at their best.
2. **Acknowledgment.** Acknowledging employees for hard work and contribution to the practice can easily motivate employees. Just simple praise from a supervisor for exhibiting a behavior that the practice values can make an employee's day. Thank-you notes can likewise increase morale.
3. **Appreciation.** Appreciation involves tangible, but not always monetary, rewards for achieving goals and excellent performance. These include traditional rewards such as certificates, tickets to sporting events, and gift cards. These rewards should be given only for a very clear reason, such as achieving a performance goal, attendance, or outstanding service to patients, and should be tailored to the recipient's personal tastes.
4. **Applause.** Applause rewards are a more public recognition and include rewards of exemplary performance. These should be saved for truly exceptional performance. These might be a ceremony or event to honor the employee. As with appreciation rewards, the applause reward should be given for a very clear reason and as such, commensurate with the accomplishment.

Many medical practices are implementing informal recognition and rewards where supervisors have the authority to give small, instantaneous tokens of appreciation without the approval of management. This type of recognition and reward should also reward special performance or achievement of a goal. These programs can be very inexpensive, and they also can be quickly implemented and easily managed. The philosophy is that it is the little things that count the most.

Exhibit 5.1 provides some recommended guidelines to use for designing or redesigning an effective recognition and reward program.

Competitive Rewards and Incentives

Offering rewards and incentives:

- Stimulates a higher level of performance;
- Recognizes employee contributions;
- Creates a positive work environment;
- Positively affects employee retention;
- Creates and identifies mentors;
- Develops, improves, and sustains morale;
- Establishes a competitive advantage; and
- Provides better service to patients.

Practice-Based vs. Performance-Based Incentives

There are two distinct types of incentive programs: those initiated by the group practice and those contingent on performance. Although performance-based programs are used less often by group practices, they are often more effective and less costly.

Group practice–initiated incentives are provided to the entire staff and thus do not reward high-level performance or directly contribute to the bottom line. These types of incentives are important for boosting morale and showing general appreciation, but they do not focus on specific, goal-oriented behavior to motivate employees. Christmas bonuses, for example, are not a reward for performance.

Other examples of group practice–initiated incentives include giving an employee flowers on his or her first day of work and giving

EXHIBIT 5.1

Reward Guidelines

Reward guidelines focus on recognizing employee performance frequently and personally, through both formal and informal means. The following tips can assist you as you develop your rewards programs:

1. **Design rewards that match your group's culture.** Rewards and incentives should reflect the practice's culture and value system.
2. **Link rewards to business goals.** Rewards should be closely aligned to practice goals and support the practice's overall strategy and mission.
3. **Allow for flexibility.** Be flexible enough to respond to change in the practice's strategic direction, economic conditions, and staff needs. Give supervisors latitude in how they recognize outstanding performance achievements and encourage on-the-spot recognition.
4. **Keep the program simple and easy to understand.** Communicate the structure and benefits of the recognition and reward program so that managers and staff can easily understand and embrace it.
5. **Match the reward to employees' performance outcomes.** Employees need to understand exactly why they are being recognized or rewarded. Otherwise, they will only experience a short-term glow without lasting impact.
6. **Be consistent in how you recognize outstanding performance.** Avoid favoritism among employees and recognize everyone who produces targeted goals. Inconsistent feedback sends confusing messages and contributes to low morale.
7. **Tailor your rewards to the recipient.** Ask recipients, as well as their colleagues, what rewards they value the most. Then let employees choose among several options. Avoid rewards that might embarrass an employee, and be sensitive to individual needs and personalities.
8. **Ensure that recognition is timely.** Timely and equitably distributed rewards are essential to stimulating outstanding performance. Very little time should lapse between the desired behavior and the corresponding recognition. The value of timely recognition is its immediacy and the likelihood that it will lead to the repeated desired behavior.
9. **Track employee achievements.** Include in the employee's file a record of outstanding performance and recognition.
10. **Recognize and reward often.** Allow employees to build on achievements and continue improving by using small perks on a regular basis, thereby creating lasting value.
11. **Review and revise your reward program.** Solicit ongoing feedback from staff making adjustments as necessary. Communicate new changes once they are approved for implementation.

turkeys and other food gifts during the holidays. Many employees celebrate staff birthdays with cards, flowers, cakes, small gifts, or potluck lunches. Other practices hold staff parties, picnics, or a planning retreat away from the office. Some employers pay for an overnight stay and then leave the second day free for fun.

At the opposite end of the spectrum are incentives contingent on performance, which directly affect the practice's overall performance and bottom line. They identify positive behaviors and are tied to the group practice's mission or specific project goals.

Formal vs. Informal Rewards

Within a practice's incentive program are rewards, which are categorized as *formal* or *informal*. Traditionally, most reward programs were highly structured and recognized above-average employee performance or milestone years of service. These formal rewards tend to be more impersonal and infrequent and lose their effectiveness over time. They create a special time when outstanding accomplishments of staff members are communicated and celebrated by the entire staff.

Group practices are increasingly offering informal reward and recognition programs, which demonstrate spontaneous appreciation of top-level performance. Not only are these programs inexpensive, but they can also be quickly implemented and easily maintained. The philosophy is that it's the little things that count the most.

Informal rewards can be categorized as *monetary* or *nonmonetary*. Monetary rewards include:

- Creating a gift closet from which top performers can select items such as coffee mugs, pen sets, movies, and music;
- Distributing tickets to sporting events, movies, concerts, or cultural events;
- Subsidizing gym memberships;
- Providing a thank-you gift basket to an employee and his or her family who worked particularly long hours on a special project;
- Giving gift certificates;
- Taking top performers to a midday movie of their choice;
- Sending employees to professional organization meetings;

- Approving educational expenses and tuition reimbursements;
- Scheduling shopping sprees and giving envelopes with cash to spend;
- Giving vouchers for professional income tax preparation;
- Giving spa services;
- Arranging for nights out on the town, including dinner and a movie; and
- Providing breakfast or lunch on busy days.

Some group practices structure rewards around the family by subsidizing diaper services, in-home tutoring, or summer day camps. Some practices hire the teenage children of staff members for administrative support during school vacations.

Monetary rewards need not involve large amounts of money. Any amount from fifty to several hundred dollars can be effective. If you use monetary rewards, separate them from the employee's regular paycheck or they may be overlooked or undervalued.

Remember that gifts up to $25, such as flowers and gift certificates, are tax deductible. Achievement rewards such as televisions, small appliances, jewelry, crystal, and china are deductible up to $400. Be sure to consult with your tax attorney or accountant because tax laws change often.

Nonmonetary rewards include:

- Putting gold stars or other recognition on employees' name badges;
- Giving time-off certificates;
- Preparing a practice or department yearbook featuring individuals and team accomplishments and photos from staff events;
- Letting top performers work flexible hours;
- Giving employees more prestigious titles when appropriate;
- Posting special achievement and thank-you letters;
- Creating a wall of fame featuring top employees' photos;
- Recognizing contributions by assigning a special parking spot;

- Highlighting top performers and their accomplishments in your practice's newsletter;
- Holding staff thank-you meetings, at which everyone thanks someone else for something they accomplished;
- Sending news releases to the local media, detailing staff's accomplishments and awards;
- Featuring top performers in the practice's printed marketing materials; and
- Washing an employee's car during lunch.

Rewarding your employees with extra time off is a very popular reward that oftentimes is valued more than money. Another benefit is that the group practice does not have to pay higher taxes because of higher salaries. Variations on how to award time off include adding time to a holiday or weekend.

Creating an Incentive or Reward Program

How best to establish an incentive or reward program that fits your group practice's needs depends on the practice's size and its philosophy on compensation, recognition, and incentives. You can start by identifying employee wants and needs through such means as employee surveys or by holding focus groups. If the practice already has an incentive or reward program in place, this is a good time to ask employees if the current program is still meaningful and how it can be improved. From this information, you can develop realistic goals for the program and identify what levels of achievement will be recognized.

Taking time to educate managers and staff about your rewards program, as well as getting their support, is critical to the success of the program. Share the thinking behind the program, the importance of recognition, and the role the program plays in helping the practice achieve its goals.

Schedule separate training and orientation programs for the management team and the rest of the staff, as each group plays a different role and has different interests in the rewards program. Explain how the program works, and then manage expectations for how performance rewards are recognized and rewarded before the implementation date. Once the program is up and running, communicate its results regularly.

Meaningful recognition should come first from the immediate supervisor, then the management team, physicians, and top administrator, as appropriate. No matter how busy your schedule, this is not the time for delegation, so never ask an associate to recognize the employee or write a note of thanks on your behalf. Part of the value of the recognition is that it comes from a manager who took his or her own time to express appreciation for a job well done. When recognizing an outstanding employee, highlight how his or her behavior affected the supervisor, the team, the department, and/or the practice. Pitfalls to avoid include:

- Offering one-size-fits-all incentives;
- Offering insincere flattery and exaggerating employees' accomplishments;
- Using incentives as a substitute for paying competitive wages;
- Giving only cash rewards;
- Overlooking employees who deserve rewards;
- Structuring performance targets that are difficult to understand;
- Sending notes of praise that also contain criticism;
- Using the same rewards repeatedly so that they lose their effectiveness;
- Telling someone they're doing a good job but failing to mention specific behaviors; and
- Giving credit for the achievements of other staff members.

The challenge today is not only revamping outdated incentive and retention programs and designing new ones, but also to continually implement, manage, and evaluate their results. Successfully implementing these programs can help your group practice retain a more motivated, productive workforce while making a significant contribution to the practice's bottom line.

Conclusion

Effective performance management systems are a medical practice administrator's best friend. Managing performance includes setting clear performance and behavior expectations, creating effective evaluation mechanisms, implementing disciplinary processes where necessary, and providing appropriate incentives and rewards for good performance.

Notes

1. Courtney Price, *HR Policies and Procedures: Manual for Medical Practices*, 5th ed. (Englewood, CO: Medical Group Management Association, 2014).
2. Courtney H. Price, *Physician Job Description Toolkit: Defining Roles for Success* (Englewood, CO: Medical Group Management Association, 2014).
3. *Uniform Guidelines on Employee Selection Procedures*, Biddle Consulting Group, 2013, www.uniformguidelines.com/uniformguidelines.html.
4. Paul Kiewiet, "What Does It Take to Engage Employees?" *Engagement Strategies Magazine*, November/December 2010, www.engagementstrategiesonline.com/What-Does-It-Take-to-Engage-Employees/.
5. Alys Novak and Courtney H. Price, *Acknowledge! Appreciate! Applaud!: 172 Easy Ways to Reward Staff for Little or No Cost* (Englewood, CO: Medical Group Management Association, 2011).

Resource List

The following resources are available on the Medical Group Management Association® (MGMA®) Website. Please visit the MGMA Store at www.mgma.org/store for updates and new products. Members of MGMA seeking assistance locating articles and industry resources on human resource management may contact the MGMA Knowledge Center at infocenter@mgma.org.

MGMA Books and Reports

- *Acknowledge! Appreciate! Applaud! 72 Easy Ways to Reward Staff for Little or No Cost,* by Alys Novak and Courtney H. Price (2011). Item # 8261.
- *Employee Handbook for Medical Practices,* by Courtney H. Price (2014). Electronic download, Item # E8804.
- *HR Policies and Procedures Manual for Medical Practices,* by Courtney H. Price (2014). Item # 8538.
- *Innovative Staffing for the Medical Practice,* by Deborah Walker Keegan (2011). Item # 8262. DVD format, Item # 8549.
- *Leadership Strategies: Achieving Personal and Professional Success,* by Ronald Menaker (2013). Item # 8707.
- *NPP Utilization in the Future of U.S. Healthcare: An MGMA Research and Analysis Report,* by MGMA (2014). Electronic download, Item # E8781.
- *Physician Contract Guidebook,* by Rade B. Vukmir (2014). Item # 8777. Electronic download, # E8777.
- *Physician Job Description Toolkit: Defining Roles for Success,* by Courtney H. Price (2013). Item # 8543.

MGMA Practice Resources Topics and Tools Sections

See the following topic-focused sections on the MGMA Website:

- Certification and Fellowship
- Human Resources
- Human Resources Tools
- MGMA Career Center
- Staffing

MGMA Connection Magazine — Human Resource Management Focus

- *Human Resource Management* issue, published each August, is an array of articles that drill down into specific Body of Knowledge domain topics.
- *Medical Practice Today*, published each July, is a review of the annually updated "What Members Have to Say" research, focusing on challenges faced by MGMA members and what they're doing to survive and thrive in today's healthcare environment.
- *The State of Medical Practice*, published each January, is an annual update to the myriad issues medical practice executives will grapple with in the coming year.

MGMA Education — Self-Study Course

- Essentials of Human Resource Management

Index

NOTE: *ex.* indicates exhibit.